OUR VILLAGE

Illustrated by the same artist

CRANFORD

OUR VILLAGE

by

MARY RUSSELL
MITFORD

George G. Harrap & Co. Ltd.

LONDON

The wood-engravings in this edition
are by
JOAN HASSALL

First published 1947
by GEORGE G. HARRAP & Co. LTD.
182 High Holborn, London, W.C. 1

Composed in Baskerville type and printed by R. & R. CLARK, LIMITED,
Edinburgh
Made in Great Britain

PUBLISHER'S NOTE

THE "Sketches of Village Life" written by Mary Russell Mitford have, since their first publication in book form, been known to their many admirers only in selections.

The first, and, indeed, most of them, were contributed to a periodical, the *Lady's Magazine*, towards the end of the first quarter of the nineteenth century; while the remainder found a wider public in some of the bijou annuals of the period — beautifully printed, daintily bound, and lavishly embellished with steel engravings — such as the *Keepsake*, the *Amulet*, the *Literary Souvenir*, *Forget-me-not*, and *Friendship's Offering*.

Selections from these essays were made and published, under the title *Our Village*, by George Whittaker, in five volumes, and in many editions of each volume, from 1824 to 1832. The success of the periodical publication of her writings led, of course, to editorial urgings to increase the series. This brought about the inclusion of much which had nothing to do with her own village. Several complete editions, with another publisher's imprint, appeared during the years between 1843 and 1856. In 1873 sixteen only of the sketches were published, still under the title *Our Village*, but some of them had no relation to the village; since that date no other selection has been prepared, the choice then made being followed slavishly. Never, until now, have there been chosen from the whole body of the essays all those which exclusively describe "our village," the village of Three Mile Cross, for so long the scene of their author's own cottage home.

In the present edition the Editor has brought together all that Miss Mitford wrote, comprised within the early editions, concerning the Berkshire village—thirty essays in all—and nothing else.

It may be of interest to mention here that the apparently erroneous spelling of certain words has been purposely retained as being in accord with that of the author and the common practice of the period; also, that the concluding essay in this present volume figured as the introductory chapter to the fifth series of the earliest collected edition.

Mr Roberts's Introduction is informed by a lifetime study of Miss Mitford's work, and Miss Joan Hassall has illuminated the scenes of rural life with sympathy and insight.

INTRODUCTION

By WILLIAM J. ROBERTS

Author of "The Life and Friendships of Mary Russell Mitford"

SOUTHWARD from Reading and three miles along the road to Basingstoke, Winchester, and the west, lies the village of Three Mile Cross, immortalized by Mary Russell Mitford as " Our Village."

Inevitably the village has changed since Miss Mitford's day— motor-cars, petrol-pumps, and Council houses have not added to its charm—but a discerning pilgrim may still find, off the beaten track, some of the old landmarks which inspired its most famous inhabitant to describe it with zest over a century ago. One may still catch the floating pungency of a wood-fire kindled on some unseen hearth, or the warm breath of cattle as they munch contentedly in their sheds at milking-time; around " Our Village " there are still great areas of open country— pastures and tillage—although tractors have largely displaced the straining teams of plodding ploughmen " tearing their innards out," as they themselves tersely put it, that used to give their one-time touch of colour to the scene. The tootling horns of the coaches are heard no more; but rooks still caw in con- clave in the high elms, still follow the ploughshare as of old, breasting the breezes and quarrelling over earth's discovered booty.

The old inns, too, remain by the roadside; so does the author's cottage; they are not so picturesque in their frontages as they were over a hundred years ago, but they happily retain some vestige of their ancient quality within doors. And Bromley's—the shop next door, " multifarious as a bazaar "— is still as it stood, having suffered little change in appearance or character; a Bromley lady (let it be added with sentimental delight) still answers the summons of the tinkling shop-door bell to serve some village urchin with brandy-balls, or his mother with candles.

Much that may be told of the author of this book was never revealed in its sparkle and high-spirited gaiety, because it was so carefully concealed. Her father, George Midford, as his

7

family then spelt their name, was of the ancient house of Midford, near Morpeth. He had studied medicine at Edinburgh University, and had been for three years a pupil of the celebrated John Hunter in London. He had also " experienced a brief career of dissipation which had reduced his pecuniary resources to a low ebb; was recklessly extravagant, and addicted to high play."

It was while on a visit to a relative—Dr Ogle, Dean of Winchester—that he was introduced to Mary Russell, ten years his senior, recently bereaved of her mother, who had bequeathed her £28,000 in cash, some land, and the house in which she was living. Despite her lack of good looks the lady was kindly, cheerful, sweet-tempered, and domesticated, qualities which, with £28,000 thrown in, made her desirable to the dashing Midford. He wooed and won her. On the assumption that her husband would qualify and set up a practice in Alresford they remained there.

Mrs Midford also came of noble stock, for she was a lineal descendant of the ducal house of Bedford, was proud of it, and adopted and used the family motto, " Che sarà sarà," a comforting or comfortless dictum, according to one's fancy. It was either the motto or her temperament which caused Mrs Midford to fold her hands in her lap when it had been better for her to be less complacent.

To this strangely assorted couple there was born a boy who lived but a few days; a year later, on December 16, 1787, came Mary, who first saw the light at Alresford, in a large house still standing in the Broad Street.

Mary's early years were extremely happy; she romped with her father and found pleasure in listening to her mother's soft and pleasing voice telling her stories. She was a precocious child; at four years of age, being perched on the breakfast-table by her father, she would read (of course without understanding it) the political jargon from one or other of the Whig newspapers, and for reward chose " not sweetmeats, but a reading of ' The Children in the Wood,' from Percy's *Reliques*," a book which in later life she averred was " the delight of my childhood, and remained to be the solace of my old age."

Although her father eventually qualified, he rarely practised; a profligate crew and the gaming tables held him. The money of his all-too-trusting wife trickled away, and creditors began to be troublesome. Much of the valuable Russell library was sold, and at last, to escape it all, the family flitted to Lyme Regis. There, true to his instincts, the gambler sought in high play to recover himself, and failed disastrously.

Discredited alike by his cronies and the tradesfolk, he fled to London, leaving his wife and child to follow as best they might. The story of their journey and its pitiful attendant misery is a shocking one. At length they reached London and found a dingy, comfortless lodging on the Surrey side of Blackfriars Bridge and, with Dr Midford, sought a refuge from creditors within the rules of the King's Bench.

Mary and her father were good companions and sometimes went sightseeing in the London streets. On one of these occasions, in celebration of her tenth birthday, her father bought her a ticket in one of the public lotteries. It proved lucky; the prize was £20,000!

Creditors were satisfied, and the family migrated to Reading, where they lived lavishly in a large house, still standing, on the London Road. Mary, sent to a boarding school in Knightsbridge, London, made good use of the experience, studied and loved the classics, reading and enjoying the works of Molière, Racine, and other dramatists in the original.

By the time she left school her father had purchased a large mansion and estate at Grazeley, about four miles south of Reading, but pulled down the house and squandered much on its rebuilding. He renamed the place " Bertram House," thereby affording himself an opportunity of hinting at his lineage and impressing the county. Moreover, just about this period— approximately the year 1802—the northern Midfords changed their name to Mitford, and the Doctor, following their lead, gained a further chance of establishing his kinship with them.

He became Chairman of the Reading Bench, later of the County Bench. His leisure was spent sometimes in coursing— the Mitford kennel was costly and renowned—sometimes in prolonged visits to London to the gambling clubs. Mary's twenty thousand pounds—she never, indeed, possessed it— dribbled away, and once again the shadow of debt made its ugly influence felt. Servants were dismissed, carriages and pictures were sold, and Mrs Mitford had occasionally to *plead with her absent spouse for a pound with which to buy bread*!

The inevitable crash came, and in a strange devil-may-care

mood Dr Mitford installed himself and his family in a labourer's cottage at Three Mile Cross, scarcely a mile from the scene of his former grandeur. It was there that Mary, now grown to womanhood, with an ailing mother becoming weaker daily and her father past redemption and lacking all initiative, determined to make the best of things and earn money by her pen. She had some success at first, but her income was small.

The letters which she wrote at this period are amazing expressions of her bravery and optimism. It needed courage to face the covertly critical county folk and to carry herself with dignity before the villagers, some of whom had no occasion to love or admire her father, Magistrate Mitford; but she had courage enough for it all. The villagers grew at last to worship her; not only the county folk, but dukes and royalty itself, vied in making her presents of plants and flowers for the big garden at the rear of the cottage, which was her greatest joy. That garden and her writing were her safety-valves.

The strangest thing in all her life, perhaps, was her unabated affection—a sort of blind worship—for her father. She has been called " a cheerful optimist, whose geese were always swans "; her father, the biggest gander of all, she regarded as majesty and grace personified! The writing of *Our Village* was one of the efforts whereby she endeavoured to pay her way and—*provide luxuries for her father*.

This joyous, intimate classic of the old happy English countryside first appeared as occasional sketches contributed to the *Lady's Magazine* of December 1822; the sketches, with their sparkle and vivacity, captivated the readers of a somewhat obscure journal, and sent up its issue with a bound from 250 to 2000 copies per month. The literary critics of the day vied with one another in praise not only of the author's easy, flowing style but of the subject-matter of the sketches, which had discovered an interest in common folk and everyday things. Harriet Martineau, the miscellaneous writer, called the work a classic, and proclaimed that the author had established a new order in literature, while Charles Lamb wrote that " nothing so fresh and characteristic has appeared for a long while."

The series ran for nearly ten years, and when at last Miss Mitford confessed that her source of supply was running dry her editor bade her seek further afield, for, said he, " the public demands it ! "

To this end she drew inspiration from the surrounding villages and hamlets, and even included the more exalted ' copy ' furnished by her aristocratic neighbours and their pursuits. Yet, whatever the subject, peer or peasant, she ever retained her sure touch for limning a character or describing a scene.

I always wrote on the spot, and at the moment and in nearly every instance with the closest and most resolute fidelity to the place and the people; painting their failures and the many virtues of the villagers, under an intense and thankful conviction that, in every condition of life, goodness and happiness may be found by those who seek them, and never more surely than in the fresh air, the shade, and the sunshine of nature.

With the publication of *Our Village* and the growing fame Miss Mitford gained thereby, Three Mile Cross became a show place. The grand literary lights made pilgrimages there; others, who scintillated in possibly higher walks of life, lined the roadside with their carriages, paying homage to the rotund, homely figure clad in the cheapest of gowns—in matters of personal adornment she had no taste.

In due course her mother, then her father, died. With his passing came freedom, but she had to pay debts amounting to a thousand pounds. Things were made easy for her by a royal bounty, and kindly, influential folk raised a fund to enable her to clear the debts.

As time went on she became a martyr to rheumatism, and a series of accidents crippled her; meanwhile the cottage at Three Mile Cross became so decrepit that it almost fell upon her. She was urged to leave it, but hesitated, for it was as a shrine wherein joys and sorrows had gone to make up her strange experience of life, and she loved it; besides, behind it lay the beloved garden! Nevertheless, it became impossible to stay, and she was forced to acquiesce in the change which she should have made earlier; she sorrowfully left the old cottage one day late in 1850 for a pleasanter one at Swallowfield, three miles farther south.

Hither came many old and cherished friends to call upon her, among them Charles Kingsley (a near neighbour), Hugh Pearson, the rector of more distant Sonning, and, best-loved of all, Lady Russell, the kindly chatelaine of the adjoining Swallowfield Park, with whom Miss Mitford shared an abiding interest in the literature of her own and other countries.

Lady Russell's visits became more frequent, her affection deeper, as Miss Mitford's strength failed; and when on January 18, 1855, shrivelled and gnarled with long suffering, she prepared to take her last journey, Lady Russell was with her, hand in hand; "Your hand, dear Lady Russell, your hand . . . ah!" she whispered as she found the last stile a little difficult of negotiation; her wonderful eyes were illumined as she spoke the words. It was as though she had suddenly emerged from the shadow of trees she loved, and found the fresh prospect more bewilderingly beautiful than she had imagined it would be!

Mary Russell Mitford's body now rests in Swallowfield Churchyard in a spot chosen by herself, the Park railings being diverted for her accommodation. It is a place of peace; the haunt of singing birds, of waving, whispering grasses; with trees that glow with colour, where primroses, violets, and cowslips give lavishly of their simple beauty. The old cottage at Three Mile Cross still stands, preserved from utter ruin by the generosity of the late William Isaac Palmer. So also does the cottage at Swallowfield, with judicious additions, but the main building is intact as in Miss Mitford's day.

The descriptive or narrative sketch exemplified in *Our Village* is not the sole form of writing which Miss Mitford tried. She had other literary interests, and during the serial run of her country sketches, through which she had become assured of a public, she turned her attention to the drama, for which, from early school-days, she had had a passion. In this field, too, she achieved some success, both Macready and Kemble producing and acting her plays in London and on tour. It is recorded that, so virile and masculine was the quality of her work, Macready could not at first believe it to be that of a woman—and a young woman at that.

Her success in this direction was short-lived, however. The plays, although perfect in phrasing and rhythm, sonorous, and at times majestic, were too sombre. It is a strange fact that they lacked the humour which was a particular attribute of the author, and which she knew so well how to display; and there was no sentimentality in them, because, as she said, it was abhorrent to her. In this she was not fair to herself.

Of all her considerable literary output the one work which

she thought least notable—*Our Village*—was, by the irony of fate, destined to become a classic and crown its writer with fame. The public of her day so decreed it; and generations of subsequent readers have supported the decree without qualification.

The popularity of the sketches made it certain that a wide circle of readers would welcome their publication in some more permanent form; a publisher willing to undertake this task was found in the person of George B. Whittaker, of Ave Maria Lane, a godson of the author's father, " a sheriff of London and a dashing young person." " I am hoping," wrote Miss Mitford to a friend,

> to get out a little volume of playful prose. You will like it, I promise you. . . . It will be called—at least I mean it so to be—*Our Village*, and will be published with, or without my name, as it shall please my worthy bibliopole. At all events, the author has no wish to be *incognita*; so I tell it to you as a secret to be told.

Our Village was published with the author's name, and Three Mile Cross was suddenly on the map. Miss Mitford's intimates, pluming themselves on their acquaintance with her home surroundings, plied her with queries as to whether their identification of scenes in the book was correct; and whether Lizzy, Joel Brent, Hannah Bint, Miss Phœbe, and the rest of the rustic characters were real, and, if so, how were they reacting to the discovery of themselves in the printed pages of a book; to one such inquirer she replied:

> You ask are the characters and descriptions true? Yes! yes! yes! as true as is well possible . . . the picture is a likeness; and that this is a very faithful one, you will judge when I tell you that a worthy neighbour of ours . . . accused me most seriously of carelessness in putting " The Rose " for " The Swan," as the sign of our next-door neighbour; and was no less disconcerted at the misprint (as he called it) of ' B ' for ' R ' as the name of our next town. *A cela près*, he declares the picture to be exact. Nevertheless, I do not expect to be poisoned. Why should I? I have said no harm of my neighbours, have I? The great danger would be that my dear friend Joel might be spoilt; but I take care to keep the book out of our pretty Harriette's way; and so I hope that prime ornament of our village will escape the snare for his vanity which the seeing so exact a portrait of himself in a printed

book might occasion. By the way, the names of the villagers are true.

The first collection to be published appeared in 1824, and as it was of a tentative character, had no indication on the title-page that other volumes were to follow. But as it proved popular, a second edition being quickly produced and sold, four additional collections were published ranging over the years 1826 to 1832. There were many reprints of each collection. The contents of the five volumes, altered only as to the sequence of the sketches, were issued in 1836, bound up in three volumes, illustrated with exquisite woodcuts, and with Whittaker continuing as publisher.

The artist responsible for the woodcuts was George Baxter, who was chosen and sent by Whittaker in 1835 to make his *sketches on the spot, under the author's supervision.* She described him as " the man so much talked of in the *Athenæum*, as the inventor of the new art of printing in colours, imitating oil paintings by engravings in wood." She also recorded that, "as artists generally are, he is a very respectable, nice man," gave him hospitality for a day and a night, with a bottle of Mr Goodlake's claret instead of port, and would have taken him out to dinner to meet Mr and Mrs Walter (he of *The Times*), but Mr Baxter excused himself by reason of the urgency of his work.

Sixteen years later this three-volume edition, complete except for a further alteration in the sequence, was published as two volumes in Bohn's Standard Library, with steel engravings as frontispieces and with Baxter's woodcuts in the text.

That edition, which was issued at regular intervals for many years, is regarded as the definitive work, and is the basis from which this present issue has been prepared. It may be permissible to suggest that were Miss Mitford alive she would, in her kindly, generous fashion, take a more than ordinary interest in this edition, which has a woman for its illustrator, who has chosen the woodcut as her medium and, like Baxter, done the sketches " on the spot."

One is almost tempted to add that the occasion might this time prompt the production of a glass of port or, mayhap, the more exclusive and lady-like stimulant—a dish of Twining's Hyson, at fourteen shillings the pound—served in Grandmamma Russell's cherished tea-set, now preserved in the Reading museum.

PREFACE

THE following pages contain an attempt to delineate country scenery and country manners, as they exist in a small village in the south of England. The writer may at least claim the merit of a hearty love of her subject, and of that local and personal familiarity, which only a long residence in one neighbourhood could have enabled her to attain. Her descriptions have always been written on the spot, and at the moment, and in nearly every instance with the closest and most resolute fidelity to the place and the people. If she be accused of having given a brighter aspect to her villagers than is usually met with in books, she cannot help it, and would not if she could. She has painted, as they appeared to her, their little frailties and their many virtues, under an intense and thankful conviction that in every condition of life goodness and happiness may be found by those who seek them, and never more surely than in the fresh air, the shade, and the sunshine of nature.

CONTENTS

ILLUSTRATIONS

OUR VILLAGE

OF all situations for a constant residence, that which appears
to me most delightful is a little village far in the country;
a small neighbourhood, not of fine mansions finely peopled, but
of cottages and cottage-like houses, " messuages or tenements,"
as a friend of mine calls such ignoble and nondescript dwellings,
with inhabitants whose faces are as familiar to us as the flowers
in our garden; a little world of our own, close-packed and
insulated like ants in an ant-hill, or bees in a hive, or sheep in
a fold, or nuns in a convent, or sailors in a ship; where we
know every one, are known to every one, interested in every
one, and authorized to hope that every one feels an interest in
us. How pleasant it is to slide into these true-hearted feelings
from the kindly and unconscious influence of habit, and to
learn to know and to love the people about us, with all their
peculiarities, just as we learn to know and to love the nooks
and turns of the shady lanes and sunny commons that we pass
every day! Even in books I like a confined locality, and so do
the critics when they talk of the unities. Nothing is so tiresome
as to be whirled half over Europe at the chariot-wheels of a
hero, to go to sleep at Vienna, and awaken at Madrid; it produces a real fatigue, a weariness of spirit. On the other hand,
nothing is so delightful as to sit down in a country village in
one of Miss Austen's delicious novels, quite sure before we leave
it to become intimate with every spot and every person it

contains; or to ramble with Mr White [1] over his own parish of Selborne, and form a friendship with the fields and coppices, as well as with the birds, mice, and squirrels, who inhabit them; or to sail with Robinson Crusoe to his island, and live there with him and his goats and his man Friday—how much we dread any newcomers, any fresh importation of savage or sailor! we never sympathize for a moment in our hero's want of company, and are quite grieved when he gets away—or to be shipwrecked with Ferdinand on that other lovelier island, the island of Prospero, and Miranda, and Caliban, and Ariel, and nobody else, none of Dryden's exotic inventions—that is best of all. And a small neighbourhood is as good in sober waking reality as in poetry or prose; a village neighbourhood, such as this Berkshire hamlet in which I write, a long, straggling, winding street at the bottom of a fine eminence, with a road through it, always abounding in carts, horsemen, and carriages, and lately enlivened by a stage-coach from B—— to S——, which passed through about ten days ago, and will I suppose return some time or other. There are coaches of all varieties nowadays; perhaps this may be intended for a monthly diligence, or a fortnight fly. Will you walk with me through our village, courteous reader? The journey is not long. We will begin at the lower end, and proceed up the hill.

The tidy, square, red cottage on the right hand, with the long well-stocked garden by the side of the road, belongs to a retired publican from a neighbouring town; a substantial person with a comely wife; one who piques himself on independence and idleness, talks politics, reads newspapers, hates the minister, and cries out for reform. He introduced into our peaceful vicinage the rebellious innovation of an illumination on the queen's acquittal. Remonstrance and persuasion were in vain; he talked of liberty and broken windows—so we all lighted up. Oh! how he shone that night with candles, and laurel, and white bows, and gold paper, and a transparency (originally designed for a pocket-handkerchief) with a flaming portrait of her Majesty, hatted and feathered, in red ochre. He had no rival in the village, that we all acknowledged; the very bonfire was less splendid; the little boys reserved their best crackers to be expended in his honour, and he gave them full

[1] White's *Natural History and Antiquities of Selborne*; one of the most fascinating books ever written. I wonder that no naturalist has adopted the same plan.

sixpence more than any one else. He would like an illumination once a month; for it must not be concealed that, in spite of gardening, of newspaper reading, of jaunting about in his little cart, and frequenting both church and meeting, our worthy neighbour begins to feel the weariness of idleness. He hangs over his gate, and tries to entice passengers to stop and chat; he volunteers little jobs all round, smokes cherry trees to cure the blight, and traces and blows up all the wasp-nests in the parish. I have seen a great many wasps in our garden to-day, and shall enchant him with the intelligence. He even assists his wife in her sweepings and dustings. Poor man! he is a very respectable person, and would be a very happy one, if he would add a little employment to his dignity. It would be the salt of life to him.

Next to his house, though parted from it by another long garden with a yew arbour at the end, is the pretty dwelling of the shoemaker, a pale, sickly-looking, black-haired man, the very model of sober industry. There he sits in his little shop from early morning till late at night. An earthquake would hardly stir him : the illumination did not. He stuck immovably to his last, from the first lighting up, through the long blaze and the slow decay, till his large solitary candle was the only light in the place. One cannot conceive anything more perfect than the contempt which the man of transparencies and the man of shoes must have felt for each other on that evening. There was at least as much vanity in the sturdy industry as in the strenuous idleness, for our shoemaker is a man of substance, he employs three journeymen, two lame, and one a dwarf, so that his shop looks like an hospital; he has purchased the lease of his commodious dwelling, some even say that he has bought it out and out; and he has only one pretty daughter, a light, delicate, fair-haired girl of fourteen, the champion, protectress, and playfellow of every brat under three years old, whom she jumps, dances, dandles, and feeds all day long. A very attractive person is that child-loving girl. I have never seen any one in her station who possessed so thoroughly that undefinable charm, the lady-look. See her on a Sunday in her simplicity and her white frock, and she might pass for an earl's daughter. She likes flowers too, and has a profusion of white stocks under her window, as pure and delicate as herself.

The first house on the opposite side of the way is the blacksmith's; a gloomy dwelling, where the sun never seems to shine; dark and smoky within and without, like a forge. The black-smith is a high officer in our little state, nothing less than a constable; but, alas! alas! when tumults arise, and the con-stable is called for, he will commonly be found in the thickest of the fray. Lucky would it be for his wife and her eight chil-dren if there were no public-house in the land: an inveterate inclination to enter those bewitching doors is Mr Constable's only fault.

Next to this official dwelling is a spruce brick tenement, red, high, and narrow, boasting, one above another, three sash-windows, the only sash-windows in the village, with a clematis on one side and a rose on the other, tall and narrow like itself. That slender mansion has a fine, genteel look. The little parlour seems made for Hogarth's old maid and her stunted footboy; for tea and card-parties—it would just hold one table; for the rustle of faded silks, and the splendour of old china; for the delight of four by honours, and a little snug, quiet scandal be-tween the deals; for affected gentility and real starvation. This should have been its destiny; but fate has been unpropitious: it belongs to a plump, merry, bustling dame, with four fat, rosy, noisy children, the very essence of vulgarity and plenty.

Then comes the village shop, like other village shops, multi-farious as a bazaar; a repository for bread, shoes, tea, cheese, tape, ribands, and bacon; for everything, in short, except the one particular thing which you happen to want at the moment, and will be sure not to find. The people are civil and thriving, and frugal withal; they have let the upper part of their house to two young women (one of them is a pretty blue-eyed girl) who teach little children their ABC, and make caps and gowns for their mammas—parcel schoolmistress, parcel mantua-maker. I believe they find adorning the body a more profitable vocation than adorning the mind.

Divided from the shop by a narrow yard, and opposite the shoemaker's, is a habitation of whose inmates I shall say no-thing. A cottage—no—a miniature house, with many additions, little odds and ends of places, pantries, and what not; all angles, and of a charming in-and-outness; a little bricked court before one half, and a little flower-yard before the other; the walls, old and weather-stained, covered with hollyhocks, roses, honey-suckles, and a great apricot-tree; the casements full of geraniums; (ah, there is our superb white cat peeping out from amongst them); the closets (our landlord has the assurance to call them rooms) full of contrivances and corner-cupboards; and the little garden behind full of common flowers, tulips, pinks, larkspurs, peonies, stocks, and carnations, with an arbour of privet, not unlike a sentry-box, where one lives in a delicious green light, and looks out on the gayest of all gay flower-beds. That house was built on purpose to show in what an exceeding small compass comfort may be packed. Well, I will loiter there no longer.

The next tenement is a place of importance, the Rose Inn; a whitewashed building, retired from the road behind its fine swinging sign, with a little bow-window room coming out on one side, and forming, with our stable on the other, a sort of open square, which is the constant resort of carts, waggons, and return chaises. There are two carts there now, and mine host is serving them with beer in his eternal red waistcoat. He is a thriving man and a portly, as his waistcoat attests, which has been twice let out within this twelvemonth. Our landlord has a stirring wife, a hopeful son, and a daughter, the belle of the village; not so pretty as the fair nymph of the shoe-shop, and far less elegant, but ten times as fine; all curl-papers in the morning, like a porcupine, all curls in the afternoon, like a poodle, with more flounces than curl-papers, and more lovers than curls. Miss Phœbe is fitter for town than country; and, to do her justice, she has a consciousness of that fitness, and turns her steps townward as often as she can. She is gone to

B—— to-day with her last and principal lover, a recruiting sergeant—a man as tall as Sergeant Kite, and as impudent. Some day or other he will carry off Miss Phœbe.

In a line with the bow-window room is a low garden-wall, belonging to a house under repair—the white house opposite the collar-maker's shop, with four lime-trees before it, and a waggon-load of bricks at the door. That house is the plaything of a wealthy, well-meaning, whimsical person, who lives about a mile off. He has a passion for brick and mortar, and, being too wise to meddle with his own residence, diverts himself with altering and re-altering, improving and re-improving, doing and undoing here. It is a perfect Penelope's web. Carpenters and bricklayers have been at work for these eighteen months, and yet I sometimes stand and wonder whether anything has really been done. One exploit in last June was, however, by no means equivocal. Our good neighbour fancied that the limes shaded the rooms, and made them dark (there was not a creature in the house but the workmen), so he had all the leaves stripped from every tree. There they stood, poor miserable skeletons, as bare as Christmas under the glowing midsummer sun. Nature revenged herself, in her own sweet and gracious manner; fresh leaves sprang out, and at nearly Christmas the foliage was as brilliant as when the outrage was committed.

Next door lives a carpenter, " famed ten miles round, and worthy all his fame "—few cabinet-makers surpass him, with his excellent wife, and their little daughter Lizzy, the plaything and queen of the village, a child three years old according to the register, but six in size and strength and intellect, in power and in self-will. She manages everybody in the place, her schoolmistress included; turns the wheeler's children out of their own little cart, and makes them draw her; seduces cakes and lollypops from the very shop window; makes the lazy carry her, the silent talk to her, the grave romp with her; does anything she pleases; is absolutely irresistible. Her chief attraction lies in her exceeding power of loving, and her firm reliance on the love and indulgence of others. How impossible it would be to disappoint the dear little girl when she runs to meet you, slides her pretty hand into yours, looks up gladly in your face, and says, " Come! " You must go: you cannot help it. Another part of her charm is her singular beauty. Together with a good deal of the character of Napoleon, she has something of his square, sturdy, upright form, with the finest limbs in the world, a complexion purely English, a round, laughing face, sunburnt and rosy, large merry blue eyes, curling brown hair, and a wonderful play of countenance. She has the imperial attitudes too, and loves to stand with her hands behind her, or folded over her bosom; and sometimes, when she has a little touch of shyness, she clasps them together on the top of her head, pressing down her shining curls, and looking so exquisitely pretty! Yes, Lizzy is queen of the village! She has

but one rival in her dominions, a certain white greyhound called Mayflower, much her friend, who resembles her in beauty and strength, in playfulness, and almost in sagacity, and reigns over the animal world as she over the human. They are both coming with me, Lizzy and Lizzy's " pretty May." We are now at the end of the street; a cross-lane, a rope-walk shaded with limes and oaks, and a cool clear pond overhung with elms, lead us to the bottom of the hill. There is still one house round the corner, ending in a picturesque wheeler's shop. The dwelling-house is more ambitious. Look at the fine flowered window-blinds, the green door with the brass knocker, and the somewhat prim but very civil person who is sending off a labouring man with sirs and curtsies enough for a prince of the blood. Those are the curate's lodgings—' apartments,' his landlady would call them; he lives with his own family four miles off, but once or twice a week he comes to his neat little parlour to write sermons, to marry, or to bury, as the case may require. Never were better or kinder people than his host and hostess; and there is a reflection of clerical importance about them, since their connexion with the Church, which is quite edifying—a decorum, a gravity, a solemn politeness. Oh, to see the worthy wheeler carry the gown after his lodger on a Sunday, nicely pinned up in his wife's best handkerchief!—or to hear him rebuke a squalling child or a squabbling woman! The curate is nothing to him. He is fit to be perpetual churchwarden.

We must now cross the lane into the shady rope-walk. That pretty white cottage opposite, which stands straggling at the end of the village in a garden full of flowers, belongs to our mason, the shortest of men, and his handsome, tall wife: he, a dwarf, with the voice of a giant—one starts when he begins to talk as if he were shouting through a speaking trumpet; she the sister, daughter, and grand-daughter, of a long line of gardeners, and no contemptible one herself. It is very magnanimous in me not to hate her; for she beats me in my own way, in chrysanthemums, and dahlias, and the like gauds. Her plants are sure to live; mine have a sad trick of dying, perhaps because I love them, " not wisely, but too well," and kill them with over-kindness. Half-way up the hill is another detached cottage, the residence of an officer, and his beautiful family. That eldest boy, who is hanging over the gate, and looking with such intense childish admiration at my Lizzy, might be a model for a Cupid.

How pleasantly the road winds up the hill, with its broad green borders and hedgerows so thickly timbered! How finely the evening sun falls on that sandy excavated bank, and touches the farm-house on the top of the eminence! and how clearly defined and relieved is the figure of the man who is just coming down! It is poor John Evans, the gardener—an excellent gardener till about ten years ago, when he lost his wife, and became insane. He was sent to St Luke's, and dismissed as cured; but his power was gone and his strength; he could no longer manage a garden, nor submit to the restraint, nor encounter the fatigue of regular employment; so he retreated to the workhouse, the pensioner and factotum of the village, amongst whom he divides his services. His mind often wanders, intent on some fantastic and impracticable plan, and lost to present objects;

but he is perfectly harmless, and full of a child-like simplicity, a smiling contentedness, a most touching gratitude.   Every one is kind to John Evans, for there is that about him which must be loved; and his unprotectedness, his utter defencelessness, have an irresistible claim on every better feeling.   I know nobody who inspires so deep and tender a pity; he improves all around him.   He is useful, too, to the extent of his little power; will do anything, but loves gardening best, and still piques himself on his old arts of pruning fruit-trees, and raising cucumbers.   He is the happiest of men just now, for he has

the management of a melon bed—a melon bed!—fie!   What a grand, pompous name was that for three melon plants under a hand-light!   John Evans is sure that they will succeed.   We shall see: as the chancellor said, " I doubt."

We are now on the very brow of the eminence, close to the Hill-house and its beautiful garden.   On the outer edge of the paling, hanging over the bank that skirts the road, is an old thorn—such a thorn!   The long sprays covered with snowy blossoms, so graceful, so elegant, so lightsome, and yet so rich! There only wants a pool under the thorn to give a still lovelier reflection, quivering and trembling, like a tuft of feathers, whiter and greener than the life, and more prettily mixed with the bright blue sky.   There should indeed be a pool; but on the dark grass-plat, under the high bank, which is crowned by that magnificent plume, there is something that does almost as well —Lizzy and Mayflower in the midst of a game at romps, " making a sun-shine in the shady place " ; Lizzy rolling, laughing, clapping her hands, and glowing like a rose; Mayflower playing about her like summer lightning, dazzling the eyes with her sudden turns, her leaps, her bounds, her attacks, and her escapes. She darts round the lovely little girl, with the same momentary touch that the swallow skims over the water, and has exactly the same power of flight, the same matchless ease and strength and grace. What a pretty picture they would make; what a pretty foreground they do make to the real landscape! The road winding down the hill with a slight bend, like that in the High-street at Oxford; a waggon slowly ascending, and a horseman passing it at a full trot—(ah! Lizzy, Mayflower will certainly desert you to have a gambol with that blood-horse!) half-way down, just at the turn, the red cottage of the lieutenant, covered with vines, the very image of comfort and content; farther down, on the opposite side, the small white dwelling of the little mason; then the limes and the rope-walk; then the village street, peeping through the trees, whose clustering tops hide all but the chimneys, and various roofs of the houses, and here and there some angle of a wall; farther on, the elegant town of B——, with its fine old church-towers and spires; the whole view shut in by a range of chalky hills; and over every part of the picture, trees so profusely scattered, that it appears like a woodland scene, with glades and villages intermixed. The trees are of all kinds and all hues, chiefly the finely-shaped elm, of so bright and deep a green, the tips of whose high outer branches drop down with such a crisp and garland-like richness, and the oak, whose stately form is just now so splendidly adorned by the sunny colouring of the young leaves. Turning again up the hill, we find ourselves on that peculiar charm of English scenery, a green common, divided by the road; the right side fringed by hedgerows and trees, with cottages and farm-houses irregularly placed, and terminated by a double avenue of noble oaks; the left, prettier still, dappled by bright pools of water, and islands of cottages and cottage-gardens, and sinking gradually down to corn-fields and meadows, and an old farm-house, with pointed roofs and clustered chimneys, looking out from its blooming orchard, and backed by woody hills. The common is itself the prettiest part of the prospect; half covered with low furze, whose golden blossoms reflect so intensely the last beams of the setting sun, and alive with cows and sheep, and two sets of cricketers; one of young men, surrounded by spectators, some standing, some sitting, some stretched on the grass, all taking a delighted interest in the game; the other, a merry group of little boys, at a humble distance, for whom even cricket is scarcely lively enough, shouting, leaping, and enjoying themselves to their hearts' content. But cricketers and country boys are too important persons in our village to be talked of merely as figures in the landscape. They deserve an individual introduction—an essay to themselves—and they shall have it. No fear of forgetting the good-humoured faces that meet us in our walks every day.

JANUARY 23RD.—At noon to-day I and my white grey-hound, Mayflower, set out for a walk into a very beautiful world—a sort of silent fairy-land—a creation of that matchless magician, the hoar-frost. There had been just snow enough to cover the earth and all its colours with one sheet of pure and uniform white, and just time enough since the snow had fallen to allow the hedges to be freed of their fleecy load, and clothed with a delicate coating of rime. The atmosphere was deliciously calm; soft, even mild, in spite of the thermometer; no perceptible air, but a stillness that might almost be felt; the sky, rather grey than blue, throwing out in bold relief the snow-covered roofs of our village, and the rimy trees that rise above them, and the sun shining dimly as through a veil, giving a pale fair light, like the moon, only brighter. There was a silence, too, that might become the moon, as we stood at our little gate looking up the quiet street; a sabbath-like pause of work and play, rare on a work-day; nothing was audible but the pleasant hum of frost, that low monotonous sound, which is perhaps the nearest approach that life and nature can make to absolute silence. The very waggons as they come down the hill along the beaten track of crisp, yellowish frost-dust glide along like shadows; even May's bounding footsteps, at her height of glee and of speed, fall like snow upon snow.

But we shall have noise enough presently: May has stopped at Lizzy's door; and Lizzy, as she sat on the window-sill with her bright rosy face laughing through the casement, has seen her and disappeared. She is coming. No! The key is turning in the door, and sounds of evil omen issue through the keyhole —sturdy " let me outs," and " I will goes," mixed with shrill cries on May and on me from Lizzy, piercing through a low continuous harangue, of which the prominent parts are apologies, chilblains, sliding, broken bones, lollypops, rods, and gingerbread, from Lizzy's careful mother. " Don't scratch the door, May! Don't roar so, my Lizzy! We'll call for you as we come back."—" I'll go now! Let me out! I will go! " are the last words of Miss Lizzy. Mem. Not to spoil that child—if I

can help it. But I do think her mother might have let the poor
little soul walk with us to-day. Nothing worse for children than
coddling. Nothing better for chilblains than exercise. Besides,
I don't believe she has any—and as to breaking her bones in
sliding, I don't suppose there's a slide on the common. These
murmuring cogitations have brought us up the hill, and half-
way across the light and airy common, with its bright expanse
of snow and its clusters of cottages, whose turf fires send such
wreaths of smoke sailing up the air, and diffuse such aromatic
fragrance around. And now comes the delightful sound of

childish voices, ringing with glee and merriment almost from
beneath our feet. Ah, Lizzy, your mother was right! They are
shouting from that deep irregular pool, all glass now, where, on
two long, smooth, liny slides, half a dozen ragged urchins are
slipping along in tottering triumph. Half a dozen steps bring
us to the bank right above them. May can hardly resist the
temptation of joining her friends, for most of the varlets are of
her acquaintance, especially the rogue who leads the slide—he
with the brimless hat, whose bronzed complexion and white
flaxen hair, reversing the usual lights and shadows of the human
countenance, give so strange and foreign a look to his flat
and comic features. This hobgoblin, Jack Rapley by name, is
May's great crony; and she stands on the brink of the steep,
irregular descent, her black eyes fixed full upon him, as if she
intended him the favour of jumping on his head. She does;
she is down, and upon him; but Jack Rapley is not easily to be
knocked off his feet. He saw her coming, and in the moment
of her leap sprung dexterously off the slide on the rough ice,
steadying himself by the shoulder of the next in the file, which

C

unlucky follower, thus unexpectedly checked in his career, fell plump backwards, knocking down the rest of the line like a nest of card-houses. There is no harm done; but there they lie, roaring, kicking, sprawling, in every attitude of comic distress, whilst Jack Rapley and Mayflower, sole authors of this calamity, stand apart from the throng, fondling, and coquetting, and complimenting each other, and very visibly laughing, May in her black eyes, Jack in his wide, close-shut mouth, and his whole monkey-face, at their comrades' mischances. I think, Miss May, you may as well come up again, and leave Master Rapley to fight your battles. He'll get out of the scrape. He is a rustic wit—a sort of Robin Goodfellow—the sauciest, idlest, cleverest, best-natured boy in the parish; always foremost in mischief, and always ready to do a good turn. The sages of our village predict sad things of Jack Rapley, so that I am sometimes a little ashamed to confess, before wise people, that I have a lurking predilection for him (in common with other naughty ones), and that I like to hear him talk to May almost as well as she does. " Come, May! " and up she springs, as light as a bird. The road is gay now; carts and post-chaises, and girls in red cloaks, and, afar off, looking almost like a toy, the coach. It meets us fast and soon. How much happier the walkers look than the riders—especially the frost-bitten gentleman, and the shivering lady with the invisible face, sole passengers of that commodious machine! Hooded, veiled, and bonneted as she is, one sees from her attitude how miserable she would look uncovered.

Another pond, and another noise of children. More sliding? Oh no! This is a sport of higher pretension. Our good neighbour, the lieutenant, skating, and his own pretty little boys, and two or three other four-year-old elves, standing on the brink in an ecstasy of joy and wonder! Oh what happy spectators! And what a happy performer! They admiring, he admired, with an ardour and sincerity never excited by all the quadrilles and the spread-eagles of the Seine and the Serpentine. He really skates well though, and I am glad I came this way; for, with all the father's feelings sitting gaily at his heart, it must still gratify the pride of skill to have one spectator at that solitary pond who has seen skating before.

Now we have reached the trees,—the beautiful trees! never so beautiful as to-day. Imagine the effect of a straight and regular double avenue of oaks, nearly a mile long, arching overhead, and closing into perspective like the roof and columns of a cathedral, every tree and branch incrusted with the bright and delicate congelation of hoar-frost, white and pure as snow, delicate and defined as carved ivory. How beautiful it is, how uniform, how various, how filling, how satiating to the eye and to the mind—above all, how melancholy! There is a thrilling awfulness, an intense feeling of simple power in that naked and colourless beauty, which falls on the earth like the thoughts of death—death pure, and glorious, and smiling,—but still death. Sculpture has always the same effect on my imagination, and painting never. Colour is life.—We are now at the end of this magnificent avenue, and at the top of a steep eminence commanding a wide view over four counties—a landscape of snow. A deep lane leads abruptly down the hill; a mere narrow cart-track, sinking between high banks clothed with fern and furze and low broom, crowned with luxuriant hedgerows, and famous for their summer smell of thyme. How lovely these banks are now—the tall weeds and the gorse fixed and stiffened in the hoar-frost, which fringes round the bright prickly holly, the pendent foliage of the bramble, and the deep orange leaves of the pollard oaks! Oh, this is rime in its loveliest form! And there is still a berry here and there on the holly, " blushing in its natural coral " through the delicate tracery, still a stray hip or haw for the birds, who abound here always. The poor birds, how tame they are, how sadly tame! There is the beautiful and rare crested wren, " that shadow of a bird," as White of Selborne calls it, perched in the middle of the hedge, nestling as it were amongst the cold bare boughs, seeking, poor pretty thing, for the warmth it will not find. And there, farther on, just under the bank, by the slender runlet, which still trickles between its transparent fantastic margin of thin ice, as if it were a thing of life—there, with a swift, scudding motion, flits, in short low flights, the gorgeous kingfisher, its magnificent plumage of scarlet and blue flashing in the sun, like the glories of some tropical bird. He is come for water to this little spring by the hillside —water which even his long bill and slender head can hardly reach, so nearly do the fantastic forms of those garland-like icy margins meet over the tiny stream beneath. It is rarely that one sees the shy beauty so close or so long: and it is pleasant to see him in the grace and beauty of his natural liberty, the only way to look at a bird. We used, before we lived in a street, to fix a little board outside the parlour window, and cover it with bread-crumbs in the hard weather. It was quite delightful to see the pretty things come and feed, to conquer their shyness, and do away their mistrust. First came the more social tribes, " the robin red-breast and the wren," cautiously, suspiciously, picking up a crumb on the wing, with the little keen bright eye fixed on the window; then they would stop for two pecks; then stay till they were satisfied. The shyer birds, tamed by their example, came next; and at last one saucy fellow of a blackbird —a sad glutton, he would clear the board in two minutes—used to tap his yellow bill against the window for more. How we loved the fearless confidence of that fine, frank-hearted creature! And surely he loved us. I wonder the practice is not more general.—" May! May! naughty May! " She has frightened away the kingfisher; and now, in her coaxing penitence, she is covering me with snow. " Come, pretty May! it is time to go home."

January 28th.—We have had rain, and snow, and frost, and rain again; four days of absolute confinement. Now it is a thaw and a flood; but our light gravelly soil, and country boots, and country hardihood, will carry us through. What a drip-ping, comfortless day it is! just like the last days of November: no sun, no sky, grey or blue; one low, overhanging, dark, dismal cloud, like London smoke—Mayflower is out coursing too, and Lizzy gone to school. Never mind. Up the hill again! Walk we must. Oh what a watery world to look back upon! Thames, Kennet, Loddon—all overflowed; our famous town, inland once, turned into a sort of Venice; C. park converted into an island; and the long range of meadows from B. to W. one huge unnatural lake, with trees growing out of it. Oh what a watery world!—I will look at it no longer. I will walk on. The road is alive again. Noise is re-born. Waggons creak, horses splash, carts rattle, and pattens paddle through the dirt with more than their usual clink. The common has its old fine tints of green and brown, and its old variety of inhabitants, horses, cows, sheep, pigs, and donkeys. The ponds are unfrozen, except where some melancholy piece of melting ice floats sul-lenly on the water; and cackling geese and gabbling ducks have replaced the lieutenant and Jack Rapley. The avenue is chill and dark, the hedges are dripping, the lanes knee-deep, and all nature is in a state of " dissolution and thaw."

THE FIRST PRIMROSE

MARCH 6TH.—Fine March weather: boisterous, bluster-
ing, much wind and squalls of rain; and yet the sky,
where the clouds are swept away, deliciously blue, with snatches
of sunshine, bright, and clear, and healthful, and the roads, in
spite of the slight glittering showers, crisply dry. Altogether the
day is tempting, very tempting. It will not do for the dear
common, that windmill of a walk; but the close sheltered lanes
at the bottom of the hill, which keep out just enough of the
stormy air, and let in all the sun, will be delightful. Past our
old house, and round by the winding lanes, and the workhouse,
and across the lea, and so into the turnpike-road again—that is
our route for to-day. Forth we set, Mayflower and I, rejoicing
in the sunshine, and still more in the wind, which gives such
an intense feeling of existence, and, co-operating with brisk
motion, sets our blood and our spirits in a glow. For mere
physical pleasure, there is nothing perhaps equal to the enjoyment of being drawn, in a light carriage, against such a wind
as this, by a blood-horse at his height of speed. Walking comes
next to it; but walking is not quite so luxurious or so spiritual,
not quite so much what one fancies of flying, or being carried
above the clouds in a balloon.

Nevertheless, a walk is a good thing; especially under this
southern hedgerow, where nature is just beginning to live again:
the periwinkles, with their starry blue flowers, and their shining
myrtle-like leaves, garlanding the bushes; woodbines and elder-
trees pushing out their small swelling buds; and grasses and
mosses springing forth in every variety of brown and green.
Here we are at the corner where four lanes meet, or rather
where a passable road of stones and gravel crosses an impassable
one of beautiful but treacherous turf, and where the small white
farm-house, scarcely larger than a cottage, and the well-stocked
rick-yard behind, tell of comfort and order, but leave all un-
guessed the great riches of the master. How he became so rich
is almost a puzzle; for, though the farm be his own, it is not
large; and though prudent and frugal on ordinary occasions,
farmer Barnard is no miser. His horses, dogs, and pigs are the

best kept in the parish—May herself, although her beauty be injured by her fatness, half envies the plight of his bitch Fly: his wife's gowns and shawls cost as much again as any shawls or gowns in the village; his dinner parties (to be sure they are not frequent) display twice the ordinary quantity of good things— two couples of ducks, two dishes of green peas, two turkey poults, two gammons of bacon, two plum-puddings; moreover, he keeps a single-horse chaise, and has built and endowed a Methodist chapel. Yet is he the richest man in these parts. Everything prospers with him. Money drifts about him like snow. He looks like a rich man. There is a sturdy squareness of face and figure; a good-humoured obstinacy; a civil importance. He never boasts of his wealth, or gives himself undue airs; but nobody can meet him at market or vestry without finding out immediately that he is the richest man there. They have no child to all this money; but there is an adopted nephew, a fine spirited lad, who may, perhaps, some day or other, play the part of a fountain to the reservoir.

Now turn up the wide road till we come to the open common, with its park-like trees, its beautiful stream, wandering and twisting along, and its rural bridge. Here we turn again, past that other white farm-house, half hidden by the magnificent elms which stand before it. Ah! riches dwell not there; but there is found the next best thing—an industrious and light-hearted poverty. Twenty years ago Rachel Hilton was the prettiest and merriest lass in the country. Her father, an old game-keeper, had retired to a village ale-house, where his good beer, his social humour, and his black-eyed daughter, brought much custom. She had lovers by the score; but Joseph White, the dashing and lively son of an opulent farmer, carried off the fair Rachel. They married and settled here, and here they live still, as merrily as ever, with fourteen children of all ages and sizes, from nineteen years to nineteen months, working harder than any people in the parish, and enjoying themselves more. I would match them for labour and laughter against any family in England. She is a blithe, jolly dame, whose beauty has amplified into comeliness: he is tall, and thin, and bony, with sinews like whipcord, a strong lively voice, a sharp weather-beaten face, and eyes and lips that smile and brighten when he speaks into a most contagious hilarity. They are very poor, and I often wish them richer; but I don't know—perhaps it might put them out.

Quite close to farmer White's is a little ruinous cottage, white-washed once, and now in a sad state of betweenity, where dangling stockings and shirts, swelled by the wind, drying in a neglected garden, give signal of a washerwoman. There dwells, at present in single blessedness, Betty Adams, the wife of our sometimes gardener. I never saw any one who so much reminded me in person of that lady whom everybody knows, Mistress Meg Merrilies—as tall, as grizzled, as stately, as dark, as gipsy-looking, bonneted and gowned like her prototype, and almost as oracular. Here the resemblance ceases. Mrs Adams is a perfectly honest, industrious, painstaking person, who earns a good deal of money by washing and charing, and spends it in other luxuries than tidiness—in green tea, and gin, and snuff. Her husband lives in a great family, ten miles off. He is a capital gardener—or rather he would be so, if he were not too ambitious. He undertakes all things, and finishes none. But a smooth tongue, a knowing look, and a great capacity of labour, carry him through. Let him but like his ale and his master, and he will do work enough for four. Give him his own way, and his full quantum, and nothing comes amiss to him.

Ah, May is bounding forward! Her silly heart leaps at the sight of the old place—and so, in good truth, does mine. What a pretty place it was—or rather, how pretty I thought it! I suppose I should have thought any place so where I had spent eighteen happy years. But it was really pretty. A large, heavy, white house, in the simplest style, surrounded by fine oaks and elms, and tall massy plantations shaded down into a beautiful lawn by wild overgrown shrubs, bowery acacias, ragged sweet-briers, promontories of dog-wood, and Portugal laurel, and bays, overhung by laburnum and bird-cherry; a long piece of water letting light into the picture, and looking just like a natural stream, the banks as rude and wild as the shrubbery, inter-spersed with broom, and furze, and bramble, and pollard oaks covered with ivy and honeysuckle; the whole enclosed by an old mossy park paling, and terminating in a series of rich meadows, richly planted. This is an exact description of the home which, three years ago, it nearly broke my heart to leave. What a tearing up by the root it was! I have pitied cabbage-plants and celery, and all transplantable things, ever since; though, in common with them, and with other vegetables, the first agony of the transportation being over, I have taken such firm and tenacious hold of my new soil, that I would not for the world be pulled up again, even to be restored to the old beloved ground—not even if its beauty were undiminished, which is by no means the case; for in those three years it has thrice changed masters, and every successive possessor has brought the curse of improvement upon the place: so that between filling up the water to cure dampness, cutting down trees to let in prospects, planting to keep them out, shutting up windows to darken the

inside of the house (by which means one end looks precisely as an eight of spades would do that should have the misfortune to lose one of his corner pips), and building colonnades to lighten the out, added to a general clearance of pollards, and brambles, and ivy, and honeysuckles, and park palings, and irregular shrubs, the poor place is so transmogrified, that if it had its old looking-glass, the water, back again, it would not know its own face. And yet I love to haunt round about it: so does May. Her particular attraction is a certain broken bank full of rabbit burrows, into which she insinuates her long pliant head and neck, and tears her pretty feet by vain scratchings: mine is a warm sunny hedgerow, in the same remote field, famous for early flowers. Never was a spot more variously flowery: prim-roses yellow, lilac white, violets of either hue, cowslips, oxlips, arums, orchises, wild hyacinths, ground ivy, pansies, straw-berries, heart's-ease, formed a small part of the Flora of that wild hedgerow. How profusely they covered the sunny open slope under the weeping birch, " the lady of the woods "—and how often have I started to see the early innocent brown snake who loved the spot as well as I did, winding along the young blossoms, or rustling amongst the fallen leaves! There are primrose leaves already, and short green buds, but no flowers; not even in that furze cradle so full of roots, where they used to blow as in a basket. No, my May, no rabbits! no primroses! We may as well get over the gate into the woody winding lane, which will bring us home again.

Here we are, making the best of our way between the old elms that arch so solemnly overhead, dark and sheltered even now. They say that a spirit haunts this deep pool—a white lady without a head. I cannot say that I have seen her, often as I have paced this lane at deep midnight, to hear the nightingales, and look at the glow-worms—but there, better and rarer than a thousand ghosts, dearer even than nightingales or glow-worms, there is a primrose, the first of the year; a tuft of primroses, springing in yonder sheltered nook, from the mossy roots of an old willow, and living again in the clear bright pool. Oh, how beautiful they are—three fully blown, and two bursting buds! How glad I am I came this way! They are not to be reached. Even Jack Rapley's love of the difficult and the unattainable would fail him here: May herself could not stand on that steep bank. So much the better. Who would wish to disturb them? There they live in their innocent and fragrant beauty, sheltered from the storms, and rejoicing in the sunshine, and looking as if they could feel their happiness. Who would disturb them? Oh, how glad I am I came this way home!

VIOLETING

MARCH 27TH.—It is a dull grey morning, with a dewy feeling in the air; fresh, but not windy; cool, but not cold;—the very day for a person newly arrived from the heat, the glare, the noise, and the fever of London, to plunge into the remotest labyrinths of the country, and regain the repose of mind, the calmness of heart, which has been lost in that great Babel. I must go violeting—it is a necessity—and I must go alone: the sound of a voice, even my Lizzy's, the touch of May-flower's head, even the bounding of her elastic foot, would disturb the serenity of feeling which I am trying to recover. I shall go quite alone, with my little basket, twisted like a bee-hive, which I love so well, because *she* gave it to me, and kept sacred to violets and to those whom I love; and I shall get out of the highroad the moment I can. I would not meet any one just now, even of those whom I best like to meet.

Ha!—Is not that group—a gentleman on a blood-horse, a lady keeping pace with him so gracefully and easily—see how prettily her veil waves in the wind created by her own rapid motion!—and that gay, gallant boy, on the gallant white Arabian, curveting at their side, but ready to spring before them every instant—is not that chivalrous-looking party Mr and Mrs M. and dear B.? No! the servant is in a different livery. It is some of the ducal family, and one of their young Etonians. I may go on. I shall meet no one now; for I have fairly left the road, and am crossing the lea by one of those wandering paths, amidst the gorse, and the heath, and the low broom, which the sheep and lambs have made—a path turfy, elastic, thymy, and sweet, even at this season.

We have the good fortune to live in an unenclosed parish, and may thank the wise obstinacy of two or three sturdy farmers, and the lucky unpopularity of a ranting madcap lord of the manor, for preserving the delicious green patches, the islets of wilderness amidst cultivation, which form, perhaps, the peculiar beauty of English scenery. The common that I am passing now—the lea, as it is called—is one of the loveliest of these favoured spots. It is a little sheltered scene, retiring, as it were, from the village; sunk amidst higher lands, hills would be almost too grand a word : edged on one side by one gay highroad, and intersected by another; and surrounded by a most picturesque confusion of meadows, cottages, farms, and orchards; with a great pond in one corner, unusually bright and clear, giving a delightful cheerfulness and daylight to the picture. The swallows haunt that pond; so do the children. There is a merry group round it now; I have seldom seen it without one. Children love water, clear, bright, sparkling water; it excites and feeds their curiosity; it is motion and life.

The path that I am treading leads to a less lively spot, to that large heavy building on one side of the common, whose solid wings, jutting out far beyond the main body, occupy three sides of a square, and give a cold, shadowy look to the court. On one side is a gloomy garden, with an old man digging in it, laid out in straight dark beds of vegetables, potatoes, cabbages, onions, beans; all earthy and mouldy as a newly dug grave. Not a flower or flowering shrub! Not a rose-tree or currant-bush! Nothing but for sober, melancholy use. Oh, how different from the long irregular slips of the cottage-gardens, with their gay bunches of polyanthuses and crocuses, their wallflowers sending sweet odours through the narrow casement, and their gooseberry-trees bursting into a brilliancy of leaf, whose vivid greenness has the effect of a blossom on the eye! Oh, how different! On the other side of this gloomy abode is a meadow of that deep, intense emerald hue, which denotes the presence of stagnant water, surrounded by willows at regular distances, and like the garden, separated from the common by a wide, moat-like ditch. That is the parish workhouse. All about it is solid, substantial, useful—but so dreary! so cold! so dark! There are children in the court, and yet all is silent. I always hurry past that place as if it were a prison. Restraint, sickness, age, extreme poverty, misery which I have no power to remove or alleviate—these are the ideas, the feelings, which the sight of those walls excites; yet, perhaps, if not certainly, they contain less of that extreme desolation than the morbid fancy is apt to paint. There will be found order, cleanliness, food, clothing, warmth, refuge for the homeless, medicine and attendance for the sick, rest and sufficiency for old age, and sympathy, the true and active sympathy which the poor show to the poor, for the unhappy. There may be worse places than a parish workhouse—and yet I hurry past it. The feeling, the prejudice, will not be controlled.

The end of the dreary garden edges off into a close-sheltered lane, wandering and winding, like a rivulet, in gentle " sinuosities " (to use a word once applied by Mr Wilberforce to the Thames at Henley), amidst green meadows, all alive with cattle, sheep, and beautiful lambs, in the very spring and pride of their tottering prettiness: or fields of arable land, more lively still with troops of stooping bean-setters, women and children, in all varieties of costume and colour; and ploughs and harrows, with their whistling boys and steady carters, going through, with a slow and plodding industry, the main business of this busy season. What work bean-setting is! What a reverse of the position assigned to man to distinguish him from the beasts of the field! Only think of stooping for six, eight, ten hours a day, drilling holes in the earth with a little stick, and then dropping in the beans one by one. They are paid according to the quantity they plant: and some of the poor women used to be accused of clumping them—that is to say, of dropping more than one bean into a hole. It seems to me, considering the temptation, that not to clump is to be at the very pinnacle of human virtue.

Another turn in the lane, and we come to the old house standing amongst the high elms—the old farm-house, which always, I don't know why, carries back my imagination to Shakespeare's days. It is a long, low, irregular building, with one room, at an angle from the house, covered with ivy, fine white-vined ivy; the first floor of the main building projecting and supported by oaken beams, and one of the windows below, with its old casement and long narrow panes, forming the half of a shallow hexagon. A porch, with seats in it, surmounted by a pinnacle, pointed roofs, and clustered chimneys, complete the picture. Alas! it is little else but a picture! The very walls are crumbling to decay under a careless landlord and ruined tenant.

Now a few yards farther, and I reach the bank. Ah! I smell them already—their exquisite perfume steams and lingers in this moist, heavy air. Through this little gate, and along the green south bank of this green wheat-field, and they burst upon me, the lovely violets, in tenfold loveliness! The ground is covered with them, white and purple, enamelling the short dewy grass, looking but the more vividly coloured under the dull, leaden sky. There they lie by hundreds, by thousands. In former years I have been used to watch them from the tiny green bud, till one or two stole into bloom. They never came on me before in such a sudden and luxuriant glory of simple beauty,—and I do really owe one pure and genuine pleasure to feverish London! How beautifully they are placed too, on this sloping bank, with the palm branches waving over them, full of early bees, and mixing their honeyed scent with the more delicate violet odour! How transparent and smooth and lusty are the branches, full of sap and life! And there, just by the old mossy root, is a superb tuft of primroses, with a yellow butterfly hovering over them, like a flower floating on the air. What happiness to sit on this tufty knoll, and fill my basket with the blossoms! What a renewal of heart and mind! To inhabit such a scene of peace and sweetness is again to be fearless, gay, and gentle as a child. Then it is that thought becomes poetry, and feeling religion. Then it is that we are happy and good. Oh, that my whole life could pass so, floating on blissful and innocent sensation, enjoying in peace and gratitude the common blessings of Nature, thankful above all for the simple habits, the healthful temperament, which render them so dear! Alas! who may dare expect a life of such happiness? But I can at least snatch and prolong the fleeting pleasure, can fill my basket with pure flowers, and my heart with pure thoughts; can gladden my little home with their sweetness; can divide my treasures with one, a dear one, who cannot seek them; can see them when I shut my eyes; and dream of them when I fall asleep.

THE COWSLIP-BALL

MAY 16TH.—There are moments in life when, without any visible or immediate cause, the spirits sink and fail, as it were, under the mere pressure of existence: moments of unaccountable depression, when one is weary of one's very thoughts, haunted by images that will not depart—images many and various, but all painful; friends lost, or changed, or dead; hopes disappointed even in their accomplishment; fruitless regrets, powerless wishes, doubt and fear, and self-distrust, and self-disapprobation. They who have known these feelings (and who is there so happy as not to have known some of them?) will understand why Alfieri became powerless, and Froissart dull; and why even needlework, the most effectual sedative, that grand soother and composer of woman's distress, fails to comfort me to-day. I will go out into the air this cool, pleasant afternoon, and try what that will do. I fancy that exercise, or exertion of any kind, is the true specific for nervousness. "Fling but a stone, the giant dies." I will go to the meadows, the beautiful meadows! and I will have my materials of happiness, Lizzy and May, and a basket for flowers, and we will make a cowslip-ball. "Did you ever see a cowslip-ball, my Lizzy?"—"No."—"Come away, then; make haste! run, Lizzy!"

And on we go, fast, fast! down the road, across the lea, past the workhouse, along by the great pond, till we slide into the deep narrow lane, whose hedges seem to meet over the water, and win our way to the little farm-house at the end. "Through the farm-yard, Lizzy; over the gate; never mind the cows; they are quiet enough."—"I don't mind 'em," said Miss Lizzy, boldly and truly, and with a proud affronted air, displeased at being thought to mind anything, and showing by her attitude and manner some design of proving her courage by an attack on the largest of the herd, in the shape of a pull by the tail. "I don't mind 'em."—"I know you don't, Lizzy; but let them alone, and don't chase the turkey-cock. Come to me, my dear!" and, for a wonder, Lizzy came.

In the meantime, my other pet, Mayflower, had also gotten

into a scrape. She had driven about a huge unwieldy sow, till the animal's grunting had disturbed the repose of a still more enormous Newfoundland dog, the guardian of the yard. Out he sallied, growling, from the depth of his kennel, erecting his tail, and shaking his long chain. May's attention was instantly diverted from the sow to this new playmate, friend or foe, she cared not which; and he of the kennel, seeing his charge unhurt, and out of danger, was at leisure to observe the charms of his fair enemy, as she frolicked round him, always beyond the reach of his chain, yet always with the natural instinctive coquetry of her sex, alluring him to the pursuit which she knew to be vain. I never saw a prettier flirtation. At last the noble animal, wearied out, retired to the inmost recesses of his habitation, and would not even approach her when she stood right before the entrance. " You are properly served, May. Come along, Lizzy. Across this wheat-field, and now over the gate. Stop! let me lift you down. No jumping, no breaking of necks, Lizzy! " And here we are in the meadows, and out of the world. Robinson Crusoe, in his lonely island, had scarcely a more complete, or a more beautiful solitude.

These meadows consist of a double row of small enclosures of rich grass-land, a mile or two in length, sloping down from high arable grounds on either side, to a little nameless brook that winds between them with a course which, in its infinite variety, clearness, and rapidity, seems to emulate the bold rivers of the north, of whom, far more than of our lazy southern streams, our rivulet presents a miniature likeness. Never was water more exquisitely tricksy—now darting over the bright pebbles, sparkling and flashing in the light with a bubbling music, as sweet and wild as the song of the woodlark; now stretching quietly along, giving back the rich tufts of the golden marsh-marigolds which grow on its margin; now sweeping round a fine reach of green grass, rising steeply into a high mound, a mimic promontory, whilst the other side sinks softly away, like some tiny bay, and the water flows between, so clear, so wide, so shallow, that Lizzy, longing for adventure, is sure she could cross unwetted; now dashing through two sand-banks, a torrent deep and narrow, which May clears at a bound; now sleeping, half hidden, beneath the alders, and hawthorns, and wild roses, with which the banks are so profusely and variously fringed, whilst flags, lilies, and other aquatic plants, almost cover the surface of the stream.[1] In good truth, it is a beautiful brook, and one that Walton himself might have sitten by and loved, for trout are there; we see them as they dart up the stream, and hear and start at the sudden plunge when they spring to the surface for the summer flies. Izaak Walton would have loved our brook and our quiet meadows; they breathe the very spirit of his own peacefulness, a soothing quietude that sinks into the soul. There is no path through them, not one; we might wander a whole spring day, and not see a trace of human habitation. They belong to a number of small proprietors, who allow each other access through their respective grounds, from pure kindness and neighbourly feeling; a privilege never abused: and the fields on the other side of the water are reached by a rough plank, or a tree thrown across, or some such homely bridge. We ourselves possess one of the most beautiful; so that the strange pleasure of property, that instinct which makes Lizzy delight in her broken doll, and May in the bare bone which she has pilfered from the kennel of her recreant admirer of Newfoundland, is added to the other charms of this enchanting scenery; a strange pleasure it is, when one so poor as I can feel it! Perhaps it is felt most by the poor, with the rich it may be less intense—too much diffused and spread out, becoming thin by expansion, like leaf-gold; the little of the poor may be not only more precious, but more pleasant to them: certain that bit of grassy and blossomy earth, with its green knolls and tufted bushes, its old pollards wreathed with ivy, and its bright and babbling waters, is very dear to me. But I must always have loved these meadows, so fresh, and cool, and delicious to the eye and to the tread, full of cowslips, and of all vernal flowers: Shakspeare's Song of Spring bursts irrepressibly from our lips as we step on them.

[1] Walking along these meadows one bright sunny afternoon, a year or two back, and rather later in the season, I had an opportunity of noticing a curious circumstance in natural history. Standing close to the edge of the stream, I remarked a singular appearance on a large tuft of flags. It looked like bunches of flowers, the leaves of which seemed dark, yet transparent, intermingled with brilliant tubes of bright blue or shining green. On examining this phænomenon more closely, it turned out to be several clusters of dragon-flies, just emerged from their deformed chrysalis state, and still torpid and motionless from the wetness of their filmy wings. Half an hour later we returned to the spot and they were gone. We had seen them at the very moment when beauty was complete and animation dormant. I have since found nearly a similar account of this curious process in Mr Bingley's very entertaining work, called *Animal Biography*.

When daisies pied, and violets blue,
    And lady-smocks all silver white,
And cuckoo-buds of yellow hue,
    Do paint the meadows with delight,
    The cuckoo then on every tree—

" Cuckoo! cuckoo! " cried Lizzy, breaking in with her clear
childish voice; and immediately, as if at her call, the real bird,
from a neighbouring tree (for these meadows are dotted with
timber like a park), began to echo my lovely little girl, " cuckoo!
cuckoo! " I have a prejudice very unpastoral and unpoetical
(but I cannot help it, I have many such) against this " har-
binger of spring." His note is so monotonous, so melancholy;
and then the boys mimic him; one hears " cuckoo! cuckoo! "
in dirty streets, amongst smoky houses, and the bird is hated
for faults not his own. But prejudices of taste, likings and dis-
likings, are not always vanquishable by reason; so, to escape
the serenade from the tree, which promised to be of considerable duration (when once that eternal song begins, on it goes
ticking like a clock)—to escape that noise I determined to excite
another, and challenged Lizzy to a cowslip-gathering: a trial
of skill and speed, to see which should soonest fill her basket.
My stratagem succeeded completely. What scrambling, what
shouting, what glee from Lizzy! twenty cuckoos might have
sung unheard whilst she was pulling her own flowers, and stealing mine, and laughing, screaming, and talking through all.

At last the baskets were filled, and Lizzy declared victor:
and down we sat, on the brink of the stream, under a spreading
hawthorn, just disclosing its own pearly buds, and surrounded
with the rich and enamelled flowers of the wild hyacinth, blue
and white, to make our cowslip-ball. Every one knows the
process: to nip off the tuft of flowerets just below the top of
the stalk, and hang each cluster nicely balanced across a
riband, till you have a long string like a garland; then to press
them closely together, and tie them tightly up. We went on
very prosperously, *considering*; as people say of a young lady's
drawing, or a Frenchman's English, or a woman's tragedy, or
of the poor little dwarf who works without fingers, or the ingenious sailor who writes with his toes, or generally of any
performance which is accomplished by means seemingly inade-
quate to its production. To be sure we met with a few accidents.
First, Lizzy spoiled nearly all her cowslips by snapping them
off too short; so there was a fresh gathering; in the next place

D

May overset my full basket, and sent the blossoms floating, like so many fairy favours, down the brook; then, when we were going on pretty steadily, just as we had made a superb wreath, and were thinking of tying it together, Lizzy, who held the riband, caught a glimpse of a gorgeous butterfly, all brown and red and purple, and skipping off to pursue the new object, let go her hold; so all our treasures were abroad again. At last, however, by dint of taking a branch of alder as a substitute for

Lizzy, and hanging the basket in a pollard-ash, out of sight of May, the cowslip-ball was finished. What a concentration of fragrance and beauty it was! golden and sweet to satiety! rich to sight, and touch, and smell! Lizzy was enchanted, and ran off with her prize, hiding amongst the trees in the very coyness of ecstasy, as if any human eye, even mine, would be a restraint on her innocent raptures.

In the meanwhile I sat listening, not to my enemy the cuckoo, but to a whole concert of nightingales, scarcely interrupted by any meaner bird, answering and vying with each other in those short delicious strains which are to the ear as roses to the eye; those snatches of lovely sound which come across us as airs from heaven. Pleasant thoughts, delightful associations, awoke as I listened; and almost unconsciously I repeated to myself the beautiful story of the Lutist and the Nightingale, from Ford's

Lover's Melancholy. Here it is. Is there in English poetry anything finer ?

Passing from Italy to Greece, the tales
Which poets of an elder time have feign'd
To glorify their Tempe, bred in me
Desire of visiting Paradise.
To Thessaly I came, and living private,
Without acquaintance of more sweet companions
Than the old inmates to my love, my thoughts,
I day by day frequented silent groves
And solitary walks.   One morning early
This accident encounter'd me : I heard
The sweetest and most ravishing contention
That art and nature ever were at strife in.
A sound of music touch'd mine ears, or rather
Indeed entranced my soul ; as I stole nearer,
Invited by the melody, I saw
This youth, this fair-faced youth, upon his lute
With strains of strange variety and harmony
Proclaiming, as it seem'd, so bold a challenge
To the clear choristers of the woods, the birds,
That as they flock'd about him, all stood silent,
Wondering at what they heard.   I wonder'd too.
A nightingale,
Nature's best skill'd musician, undertakes
The challenge ; and for every several strain
The well-shaped youth could touch, she sang him down.
He could not run divisions with more art
Upon his quaking instrument than she,
The nightingale, did with her various notes
Reply to.
Some time thus spent, the young man grew at last
Into a pretty anger, that a bird,
Whom art had never taught cliffs, moods, or notes,
Should vie with him for mastery, whose study
Had busied many hours to perfect practice.
To end the controversy, in a rapture
Upon his instrument he plays so swiftly,
So many voluntaries, and so quick,
That there was curiosity and cunning,
Concord in discord, lines of differing method
Meeting in one full centre of delight.
The bird (ordain'd to be
Music's first martyr) strove to imitate
These several sounds ; which when her warbling throat
Fail'd in, for grief down dropt she on his lute,
And brake her heart.   It was the quaintest sadness
To see the conqueror upon her hearse
To weep a funeral elegy of tears.
He look'd upon the trophies of his art,

Then sigh'd, then wiped his eyes ; then sigh'd, and cry'd
" Alas ! poor creature, I will soon revenge
This cruelty upon the author of it.
Henceforth this lute, guilty of innocent blood,
Shall never more betray a harmless peace
To an untimely end " : and in that sorrow,
As he was pashing it against a tree,
I suddenly stept in.

When I had finished the recitation of this exquisite passage, the sky, which had been all the afternoon dull and heavy, began to look more and more threatening; darker clouds, like wreaths of black smoke, flew across the dead leaden tint; a cooler, damper air blew over the meadows, and a few large heavy drops splashed in the water. " We shall have a storm. Lizzy! May! where are ye? Quick, quick, my Lizzy! run, run! faster, faster! "

And off we ran; Lizzy not at all displeased at the thoughts of a wetting, to which indeed she is almost as familiar as a duck; May, on the other hand, peering up at the weather, and shaking her pretty ears with manifest dismay. Of all animals, next to a cat, a greyhound dreads rain. She might have escaped it; her light feet would have borne her home long before the shower; but May is too faithful for that, too true a comrade, understands too well the laws of good-fellowship; so she waited for us. She did, to be sure, gallop on before, and then stop and look back, and beckon as it were, with some scorn in her black eyes at the slowness of our progress. We in the meanwhile got on as fast as we could, encouraging and reproaching each other. " Faster, my Lizzy! Oh, what a bad runner! "—" Faster, faster! Oh, what a bad runner! " echoed my saucebox. " You are so fat, Lizzy, you make no way! "— " Ah! who else is fat? " retorted the darling. Certainly her mother is right; I do spoil that child.

By this time we were thoroughly soaked, all three. It was a pelting shower, that drove through our thin summer clothing and poor May's short glossy coat in a moment. And then, when we were wet to the skin, the sun came out, actually the sun, as if to laugh at our plight; and then, more provoking still, when the sun was shining, and the shower over, came a maid and a boy to look after us, loaded with cloaks and umbrellas enough to fence us against a whole day's rain. Never mind! on we go, faster and faster; Lizzy obliged to be most ignobly carried, having had the misfortune to lose a shoe in the mud, which we left the boy to look after.

Here we are at home—dripping; but glowing and laughing, and bearing our calamity most manfully. May, a dog of excellent sense, went instantly to bed in the stable, and is at this moment over head and ears in straw; Lizzy is gone to bed too, coaxed into that wise measure by a promise of tea and toast, and of not going home till to-morrow, and the story of Little Red Riding-Hood; and I am enjoying the luxury of dry clothing by a good fire. Really getting wet through now and then is no bad thing, finery apart; for one should not like spoiling a new pelisse, or a handsome plume; but when there is nothing in question but a white gown and a straw bonnet, as was the case to-day, it is rather pleasant than not. The little chill refreshes, and our enjoyment of the subsequent warmth and dryness is positive and absolute. Besides, the stimulus and exertion do good to the mind as well as body. How melancholy I was all the morning! how cheerful I am now! Nothing like a shower-bath—a real shower-bath, such as Lizzy and May and I have undergone—to cure low spirits. Try it, my dear readers, if ever ye be nervous—I will answer for its success.

THE HARD SUMMER

AUGUST 15TH.—Cold, cloudy, windy, wet. Here we are, in the midst of the dog-days, clustering merrily round the warm hearth like so many crickets, instead of chirruping in the green fields like that other merry insect the grasshopper; shivering under the influence of the *Jupiter Pluvius* of England, the watery St Swithin; peering at that scarce personage the sun, when he happens to make his appearance, as intently as astronomers look after a comet, or the common people stare at a balloon; exclaiming against the cold weather, just as we used to exclaim against the warm. " What a change from last year ! " is the first sentence you hear, go where you may. Everybody remarks it, and everybody complains of it; and yet in my mind it has its advantages, or at least its compensations, as everything in Nature has, if we would only take the trouble to seek for them.

Last year, in spite of the love which we are now pleased to profess towards that ardent luminary, not one of the sun's numerous admirers had courage to look him in the face : there was no bearing the world till he had said " Good-night " to it. Then we might stir : then we began to wake and to live. All day long we languished under his influence in a strange dreaminess, too hot to work, too hot to read, too hot to write, too hot even to talk; sitting hour after hour in a green arbour, embowered in leafiness, letting thought and fancy float as they would. Those day-dreams were pretty things in their way; there is no denying that. But then, if one half of the world were to dream through a whole summer, like the sleeping Beauty in the wood, what would become of the other ?

The only office requiring the slightest exertion, which I performed in that warm weather, was watering my flowers. Common sympathy called for that labour. The poor things withered, and faded, and pined away; they almost, so to say, panted for drought. Moreover, if I had not watered them myself, I suspect that no one else would; for water last year was nearly as precious hereabout as wine. Our land-springs were dried up; our wells were exhausted; our deep ponds

were dwindling into mud; and geese, and ducks, and pigs,
and laundresses, used to look with a jealous and suspicious eye
on the few and scanty half-buckets of that impure element,
which my trusty lacquey was fain to filch for my poor geraniums
and campanulas and tuberoses. We were forced to smuggle
them in through my faithful adherent's territories, the stable,
to avoid lectures within doors; and at last even that resource
failed; my garden, my blooming garden, the joy of my eyes,
was forced to go waterless like its neighbours, and became
shrivelled, scorched, and sunburnt, like them. It really went
to my heart to look at it.

On the other side of the house matters were still worse. What
a dusty world it was, when about sunset we became cool enough
to creep into it! Flowers in the court looking fit for a *hortus
siccus*; mummies of plants, dried as in an oven; hollyhocks,
once pink, turned into Quakers; cloves smelling of dust. Oh
dusty world! May herself looked of that complexion; so did
Lizzy; so did all the houses, windows, chickens, children, trees,
and pigs in the village; so above all did the shoes. No foot
could make three plunges into that abyss of pulverized gravel,
which had the impudence to call itself a hard road, without
being clothed with a coat a quarter of an inch thick. Woe to
white gowns! woe to black! Drab was your only wear.

Then, when we were out of the street, what a toil it was to
mount the hill, climbing with weary steps and slow upon the
brown turf by the wayside, slippery, hot, and hard as a rock!
And then if we happened to meet a carriage coming along the
middle of the road—the bottomless middle—what a sandy whirl-
wind it was! What choking! what suffocation! No state could
be more pitiable, except indeed that of the travellers who carried
this misery about with them. I shall never forget the plight in
which we met the coach one evening in last August, full an
hour after its time, steeds and driver, carriage, and passengers,
all one dust. The outsides, and the horses, and the coachman,
seemed reduced to a torpid quietness, the resignation of despair.
They had left off trying to better their condition, and taken
refuge in a wise and patient hopelessness, bent to endure in
silence the extremity of ill. The six insides, on the contrary,
were still fighting against their fate, vainly struggling to
ameliorate their hapless destiny. They were visibly grumbling
at the weather, scolding at the dust, and heating themselves

like a furnace, by striving against the heat. How well I remember the fat gentleman without his coat, who was wiping
his forehead, heaving up his wig, and certainly uttering that
English ejaculation, which, to our national reproach, is the
phrase of our language best known on the continent. And that
poor boy, red-hot, all in a flame, whose mamma, having divested
her own person of all superfluous apparel, was trying to relieve
his sufferings by the removal of his neckerchief—an operation
which he resisted with all his might. How perfectly I remember
him, as well as the pale girl who sat opposite, fanning herself
with her bonnet into an absolute fever! They vanished after a
while into their own dust; but I have them all before my eyes
at this moment, a companion picture to Hogarth's Afternoon,
a standing lesson to the grumblers at cold summers.

For my part, I really like this wet season. It keeps us within,
to be sure, rather more than is quite agreeable; but then we
are at least awake and alive there, and the world out of doors
is so much the pleasanter when we can get abroad. Everything
does well, except those fastidious bipeds, men and women; corn
ripens, grass grows, fruit is plentiful; there is no lack of birds
to eat it, and there has not been such a wasp season these dozen
years. My garden wants no watering, and is more beautiful
than ever, beating my old rival in that primitive art, the pretty
wife of the little mason, out and out. Measured with mine, her
flowers are nought. Look at those hollyhocks, like pyramids of
roses; those garlands of the convolvulus major of all colours,
hanging around that tall pole, like the wreathy hop-bine; those
magnificent dusky cloves, breathing of the Spice Islands; those
flaunting double dahlias; those splendid scarlet geraniums, and
those fierce and warlike flowers the tiger-lilies. Oh how beautiful they are! Besides, the weather clears sometimes—it has
cleared this evening; and here are we, after a merry walk up
the hill, almost as quick as in the winter, bounding lightly along
the bright green turf of the pleasant common, enticed by the
gay shouts of a dozen clear young voices, to linger awhile, and
see the boys play at cricket.

I plead guilty to a strong partiality towards that unpopular
class of beings, country boys: I have a large acquaintance
amongst them, and I can almost say, that I know good of many
and harm of none. In general they are an open, spirited, good-
humoured race, with a proneness to embrace the pleasures and

eschew the evils of their condition, a capacity for happiness, quite unmatched in man, or woman, or girl. They are patient, too, and bear their fate as scape-goats (for all sins whatsoever are laid as matters of course to their door), whether at home or abroad, with amazing resignation; and, considering the many lies of which they are the objects, they tell wonderfully few in return. The worst that can be said of them is, that they seldom, when grown to man's estate, keep the promise of their boyhood; but that is a fault to come—a fault that may not come, and ought not to be anticipated. It is astonishing how sensible they are to notice from their betters, or those whom they think such. I do not speak of money, or gifts, or praise, or the more coarse and common briberies—they are more delicate courtiers; a word, a nod, a smile, or the mere calling of them by their names, is enough to insure their hearts and their services. Half a dozen of them, poor urchins, have run away now to bring us chairs from their several homes. " Thank you, Joe Kirby!—you are always first—yes, that is just the place—I shall see everything there. Have you been in yet, Joe ?"— " No, ma'am! I go in next."—" Ah, I am glad of that—and now's the time. Really that was a pretty ball of Jem Eusden's! —I was sure it would go to the wicket. Run, Joe! They are waiting for you." There was small need to bid Joe Kirby make haste; I think he is, next to a racehorse, or a greyhound, or a deer, the fastest creature that runs—the most completely alert and active. Joe is mine especial friend, and leader of the " tender juveniles," as Joel Brent is of the adults. In both instances this post of honour was gained by merit, even more remarkably so in Joe's case than in Joel's; for Joe is a less boy than many of his companions (some of whom are fifteeners and sixteeners, quite as tall and nearly as old as Tom Coper), and a poorer than all, as may be conjectured from the lamentable state of that patched round frock, and the ragged condition of those unpatched shoes, which would encumber, if anything could, the light feet that wear them. But why should I lament the poverty that never troubles him? Joe is the merriest and happiest creature that ever lived twelve years in this wicked world. Care cannot come near him. He hath a perpetual smile on his round ruddy face, and a laugh in his hazel eye, that drives the witch away. He works at yonder farm on the top of the hill, where he is in such repute for intelligence and good-humour, that he has the honour of performing all the errands of the house, of helping the maid, the mistress, and the master, in addition to his own stated office of carter's boy. There he works hard from five till seven, and then he comes here to work still harder, under the name of play—batting, bowling, and fielding, as if for life, filling the place of four boys; being, at a pinch, a whole eleven. The late Mr Knyvett, the king's organist, who used in his own person to sing twenty parts at once of the *Hallelujah Chorus*, so that you would have thought he had a nest of nightingales in his throat, was but a type of Joe Kirby. There is a sort of ubiquity about him; he thinks nothing of being in two places at once, and for pitching a ball, William Grey himself is nothing to him. It goes straight to the mark like a bullet. He is king of the cricketers from eight to sixteen, both inclusive, and an excellent ruler he makes. Nevertheless, in the best-ordered states there will be grumblers, and we have an opposition here in the shape of Jem Eusden.

Jem Eusden is a stunted lad of thirteen, or thereabout, lean, small, and short, yet strong and active. His face is of an extraordinary ugliness, colourless, withered, haggard, with a look of extreme age, much increased by hair so light that it might rather pass for white than flaxen. He is constantly arrayed in the blue cap and old-fashioned coat, the costume of an endowed school to which he belongs; where he sits still all day, and rushes into the field at night, fresh, untired, and ripe for action, to scold, and brawl, and storm, and bluster. He hates Joe Kirby, whose immovable good-humour, broad smiles, and knowing nods, must certainly be very provoking to so fierce and turbulent a spirit; and he has himself (being, except by rare accident, no great player) the preposterous ambition of wishing to be manager of the sports. In short, he is a demagogue in embryo, with every quality necessary to a splendid success in that vocation—a strong voice, a fluent utterance, an incessant iteration, and a frontless impudence. He is a great " scholar " too, to use the country phrase; his " piece," as our village schoolmaster terms a fine sheet of flourishing writing, something between a valentine and a sampler, enclosed within a border of little coloured prints—his last, I remember, was encircled by an engraved history of Moses, beginning at the finding in the bulrushes, with Pharaoh's daughter dressed in a rose-coloured gown and blue feathers—his piece is not only the admiration of

the school, but of the parish, and is sent triumphantly round
from house to house at Christmas, to extort halfpence and six-
pences from all encouragers of learning—*Montem* in miniature.
The Mosaic history was so successful, that the produce enabled
Jem to purchase a bat and ball, which, besides adding to his
natural arrogance (for the little pedant actually began to mutter
against being eclipsed by a dunce, and went so far as to challenge
Joe Kirby to a trial in Practice, or the Rule of Three) gave him,
when compared with the general poverty, a most unnatural
preponderance in the cricket state. He had the ways and means
in his hands—(for alas! the hard winter had made sad havoc
among the bats, and the best ball was a bad one)—he had the
ways and means, could withhold the supplies, and his party was
beginning to wax strong, when Joe received a present of two
bats and a ball for the youngsters in general, and himself in
particular—and Jem's adherents left him on the spot—they
ratted, to a man, that very evening. Notwithstanding this
desertion, their forsaken leader has in nothing relaxed from his
pretensions, or his ill-humour. He still quarrels and brawls as
if he had a faction to back him, and thinks nothing of contend-
ing with both sides, the ins and the outs, secure of out-talking
the whole field. He has been squabbling these ten minutes,
and is just marching off now with his own bat (he has never
deigned to use one of Joe's) in his hand. What an ill-conditioned
hobgoblin it is! And yet there is something bold and sturdy
about him too. I should miss Jem Eusden.

Ah, there is another deserter from the party! my friend the
little hussar—I do not know his name, and call him after his
cap and jacket. He is a very remarkable person, about the
age of eight years, the youngest piece of gravity and dignity I
ever encountered; short, and square, and upright, and slow,
with a fine bronzed flat visage, resembling those convertible
signs the Broad-Face and the Saracen's-Head, which, happening to be next-door neighbours in the town of B., I never know
apart, resembling, indeed, any face that is open-eyed and immovable, the very sign of a boy! He stalks about with his hands
in his breeches pocket, like a piece of machinery; sits leisurely
down when he ought to field, and never gets farther in batting
than to stop the ball. His is the only voice never heard in the
mêlée: I doubt, indeed, if he have one, which may be partly
the reason of a circumstance that I record to his honour, his

fidelity to Jem Eusden, to whom he has adhered through every change of fortune, with a tenacity proceeding perhaps from an instinctive consciousness that the loquacious leader talks enough for two. He is the only thing resembling a follower that our demagogue possesses, and is cherished by him accordingly. Jem quarrels for him, scolds for him, pushes for him; and but for Joe Kirby's invincible good-humour, and a just discrimination of the innocent from the guilty, the activity of Jem's friendship would get the poor hussar ten drubbings a day.

But it is growing late. The sun has set a long time. Only see what a gorgeous colouring has spread itself over those parting masses of clouds in the west—what a train of rosy light! We shall have a fine sunshiny day to-morrow—a blessing not to be undervalued, in spite of my late vituperation of heat. Shall we go home now? And shall we take the longest but prettiest road, that by the green lanes? This way, to the left, round the corner of the common, past Mr Welles's cottage, and our path lies straight before us. How snug and comfortable that cottage looks! Its little yard all alive with the cow, and the mare, and the colt almost as large as the mare, and the young foal, and the great yard-dog, all so fat! Fenced in with hay-rick, and wheat-rick, and bean-stack, and backed by the long garden, the spacious drying-ground, the fine orchard, and that large field quartered into four different crops. How comfortable this cottage looks, and how well the owners earn their comforts! They are the most prosperous pair in the parish—she a laundress with twenty times more work than she can do, unrivalled in flounces and shirt-frills, and such delicacies of the craft; he, partly a farmer, partly a farmer's man, tilling his own ground, and then tilling other people's—affording a proof, even in this declining age, when the circumstances of so many worthy members of the community seem to have " an alacrity in sinking," that it is possible to amend them by sheer industry. He, who was born in the workhouse, and bred up as a parish boy, has now, by mere manual labour, risen to the rank of a land-owner, pays rates and taxes, grumbles at the times, and is called Master Welles—the title next to Mister—that by which Shakspeare was called— what would man have more? His wife, besides being the best laundress in the county, is a comely woman still. There she stands at the spring, dipping up water for to-morrow—the clear, deep, silent spring, which sleeps so peacefully under its high flowery bank, red with the tall spiral stalks of the foxglove and their rich pendent bells, blue with the beautiful forget-me-not, that gem-like blossom, which looks like a living jewel of turquoise and topaz. It is almost too late to see its beauty; and here is the pleasant shady lane, where the high elms will shut out the little twilight that remains. Ah, but we shall have the fairies' lamps to guide us, the stars of the earth, the glow-worms! Here they are, three almost together. Do you not see them? One seems tremulous, vibrating, as if on the extremity of a leaf of grass; the others are deeper in the hedge, in some green cell on which their light falls with an emerald lustre. I hope my friends the cricketers will not come this way home. I would not have the pretty creatures removed for more than I care to say, and in this matter I would hardly trust Joe Kirby—boys so love to stick them in their hats. But this lane is quite deserted. It is only a road from field to field. No one comes here at this hour. They are quite safe; and I shall walk here to-morrow and visit them again. And now, good night! beautiful insects, lamps of the fairies, good night!

NUTTING

SEPTEMBER 26TH.—One of those delicious autumnal days, when the air, the sky, and the earth seem lulled into a universal calm, softer and milder even than May. We sallied forth for a walk, in a mood congenial to the weather and the season, avoiding, by mutual consent, the bright and sunny common, and the gay highroad, and stealing through shady, unfrequented lanes, where we were not likely to meet any one—not even the pretty family procession which in other years we used to contemplate with so much interest—the father, mother, and children, returning from the wheat-field, the little ones laden with bristling close-tied bunches of wheat-ears, their own gleanings, or a bottle and a basket which had contained their frugal dinner, whilst the mother would carry her babe hushing and lulling it, and the father and an elder child trudged after with the cradle, all seeming weary, and all happy. We shall not see such a procession as this to-day; for the harvest is nearly over, the fields are deserted, the silence may almost be felt. Except the wintry notes of the redbreast, nature herself is mute. But how beautiful, how gentle, how harmonious, how rich! The rain has preserved to the herbage all the freshness and verdure of spring, and the world of leaves has lost nothing of its midsummer brightness, and the harebell is on the banks, and the woodbine in the hedges, and the low furze, which the lambs cropped in the spring, has burst again into its golden blossoms.

All is beautiful that the eye can see; perhaps the more beautiful for being shut in with a forest-like closeness. We have no prospect in this labyrinth of lanes, cross-roads, mere cartways, leading to the innumerable little farms into which this part of the parish is divided. Up-hill or down, these quiet woody lanes scarcely give us a peep at the world, except when, leaning over a gate, we look into one of the small enclosures, hemmed in with hedgerows, so closely set with growing timber, that the meady opening looks almost like a glade in a wood; or when some cottage, planted at a corner of one of the little greens formed by the meeting of these cross-ways, almost startles us by the unexpected sight of the dwellings of men in such a solitude. But that we have more of hill and dale, and that our cross-roads are excellent in their kind, this side of our parish would resemble the description given of La Vendée, in Madame Laroche-Jacquelin's most interesting book.[1] I am sure if wood can entitle a country to be called Le Bocage, none can have a better right to the name. Even this pretty snug farm-house on the hillside, with its front covered with the rich vine, which goes wreathing up to the very top of the clustered chimney, and its sloping orchard full of fruit—even this pretty quiet nest can hardly peep out of its leaves. Ah! they are gathering in the

orchard harvest. Look at that young rogue in the old mossy apple-tree—that great tree, bending with the weight of its golden-rennets—see how he pelts his little sister beneath with apples as red and as round as her own cheeks, while she, with her outstretched frock, is trying to catch them, and laughing and offering to pelt again as often as one bobs against her; and look at that still younger imp, who, as grave as a judge, is creeping on hands and knees under the tree, picking up the apples as they fall so deedily,[2] and depositing them so honestly in the great basket on the grass, already fixed so firmly and

[1] An almost equally interesting account of that very peculiar and interesting scenery may be found in *The Maid of La Vendée*, an English novel, remarkable for its simplicity and truth of painting, written by Mrs Le Noir, the daughter of Christopher Smart, an inheritrix of much of his talent. Her works deserve to be better known.

[2] " Deedily "—I am not quite sure that this word is good English; but it is genuine Hampshire, and is used by the most correct of female writers, Miss Austen. It means (and it is no small merit that it has no exact synonyme) anything done with a profound and plodding attention, an action which engrosses all the powers of mind and body.

opened so widely, and filled almost to overflowing by the brown rough fruitage of the golden-rennet's next neighbour the russeting; and see that smallest urchin of all, seated apart in infantine state on the turfy bank, with that toothsome piece of deformity a crumpling in each hand now biting from one sweet, hard, juicy morsel and now from another.—Is not that a pretty English picture? And then, farther up the orchard, that bold hardy lad, the eldest-born, who has scaled (Heaven knows how!) the tall, straight upper branch of that great pear-tree, and is sitting there as securely and as fearlessly, in as much real safety and apparent danger, as a sailor on the top-mast. Now he shakes the tree with a mighty swing that brings down a pelting shower of stony bergamots, which the father gathers rapidly up, whilst the mother can hardly assist for her motherly fear—a fear which only spurs the spirited boy to bolder ventures. Is not that a pretty picture? And they are such a handsome family too, the Brookers. I do not know that there is any gipsy blood, but there is the true gipsy complexion, richly brown, with cheeks and lips so deeply red, black hair curling close to their heads in short crisp rings, white shining teeth—and such eyes!—That sort of beauty entirely eclipses your mere roses and lilies. Even Lizzy, the prettiest of fair children, would look poor and watery by the side of Willy Brooker, the sober little personage who is picking up the apples with his small chubby hands, and filling the basket so orderly, next to his father the most useful man in the field. " Willy! " He hears without seeing; for we are quite hidden by the high bank, and a spreading hawthorn bush that over-tops it, though between the lower branches and the grass we have found a convenient peep-hole. " Willy! " The voice sounds to him like some fairy dream, and the black eyes are raised from the ground with sudden wonder, the long silky eye-lashes thrown back till they rest on the delicate brow, and a deeper blush is burning on those dark cheeks, and a smile is dimpling about those scarlet lips. But the voice is silent now, and the little quiet boy, after a moment's pause, is gone coolly to work again. He is indeed a most lovely child. I think some day or other he must marry Lizzy; I shall propose the match to their respective mammas. At present the parties are rather too young for a wedding—the intended bridegroom being, as I should judge, six, or thereabout, and the fair bride barely five —but at least we might have a betrothment after the royal fashion—there could be no harm in that. Miss Lizzy, I have no doubt, would be as demure and coquettish as if ten winters more had gone over her head, and poor Willy would open his innocent black eyes, and wonder what was going forward. They would be the very Oberon and Titania of the village, the fairy king and queen.

Ah! here is the hedge along which the periwinkle wreathes and twines so profusely, with its evergreen leaves shining like the myrtle, and its starry blue flowers. It is seldom found wild in this part of England; but, when we do meet with it, it is so abundant and so welcome—the very robin-redbreast of flowers, a winter friend. Unless in those unfrequent frosts which destroy all vegetation, it blossoms from September to June, surviving the last lingering crane's-bill, forerunning the earliest primrose, hardier even than the mountain daisy—peeping out from beneath the snow, looking at itself in the ice, smiling through the tempests of life, and yet welcoming and enjoying the sunbeams. Oh, to be like that flower!

The little spring that has been bubbling under the hedge all along the hillside, begins, now that we have mounted the eminence and are imperceptibly descending, to deviate into a capricious variety of clear deep pools and channels, so narrow and so choked with weeds, that a child might overstep them. The hedge has also changed its character. It is no longer the close compact vegetable wall of hawthorn, and maple, and brier-roses, intertwined with bramble and woodbine, and crowned with large elms or thickly set saplings. No! the pretty meadow which rises high above us, backed and almost surrounded by a tall coppice, needs no defence on our side but its own steep bank, garnished with tufts of broom, with pollard oaks wreathed with ivy, and here and there with long patches of hazel overhanging the water. "Ah, there are still nuts on that bough!" and in an instant my dear companion, active and eager and delighted as a boy, has hooked down with his walking-stick one of the lissome hazel stalks, and cleared it of its tawny clusters, and in another moment he has mounted the bank, and is in the midst of the nuttery, now transferring the spoil from the lower branches into that vast variety of pockets which gentlemen carry about them, now bending the tall tops into the lane, holding them down by main force, so that I might reach them and enjoy the pleasure of collecting some of the

E

plunder myself. A very great pleasure he knew it would be. I doffed my shawl, tucked up my flounces, turned my straw bonnet into a basket, and began gathering and scrambling—for, manage it how you may, nutting is scrambling work—those boughs, however tightly you may grasp them by the young fragrant twigs and the bright green leaves, will recoil and burst away; but there is a pleasure even in that: so on we go, scrambling and gathering with all our might and all our glee. Oh what an enjoyment! All my life long I have had a passion for that sort of seeking which implies finding (the secret, I believe, of the love of field-sports, which is in man's mind a natural impulse)—therefore I love violeting—therefore, when we had a fine garden, I used to love to gather strawberries, and cut asparagus, and, above all, to collect the filberts from the shrubberies: but this hedgerow nutting beats that sport all to nothing. That was a make-believe thing, compared with this; there was no surprise, no suspense, no unexpectedness—it was as inferior to this wild nutting, as the turning out of a bag-fox is to unearthing the fellow, in the eyes of a staunch fox-hunter.

Oh what enjoyment this nut-gathering is! They are in such abundance, that it seems as if there were not a boy in the parish, nor a young man, nor a young woman—for a basket of nuts is the universal tribute of country gallantry; our pretty damsel Harriet has had at least half a dozen this season; but no one has found out these. And they are so full too, we lose half of them from over-ripeness; they drop from the socket at the slightest motion. If we lose, there is one who finds. May is as fond of nuts as a squirrel, and cracks the shell and extracts the kernel with equal dexterity. Her white glossy head is upturned now to watch them as they fall. See how her neck is thrown back like that of a swan, and how beautifully her folded ears quiver with expectation, and how her quick eye follows the rustling noise, and her light feet dance and pat the ground, and leap up with eagerness, seeming almost sustained in the air, just as I have seen her when Brush is beating a hedgerow, and she knows from his questing that there is a hare afoot. See, she has caught that nut just before it touched the water; but the water would have been no defence—she fishes them from the bottom, she delves after them amongst the matted grass—even my bonnet—how beggingly she looks at that! " Oh what a pleasure nutting is!—Is it not, May? But the pockets are almost full and so is the basket-bonnet, and that bright watch the sun says it is late; and after all it is wrong to rob the poor boys—is it not, May? "—May shakes her graceful head denyingly, as if she understood the question—" And we must go home now—must we not? But we will come nutting again some time or other—shall we not, my May? "

THE VISIT

OCTOBER 27TH.—A lovely autumnal day; the air soft, balmy, genial; the sky of that softened and delicate blue upon which the eye loves to rest—the blue which gives such relief to the rich beauty of the earth, all around glowing in the ripe and mellow tints of the most gorgeous of the seasons. Really such an autumn may well compensate our English climate for the fine spring of the south, that spring of which the poets talk, but which we so seldom enjoy. Such an autumn glows upon us like a splendid evening; it is the very sunset of the year; and I have been tempted forth into a wider range of enjoyment than usual. This *walk* (if I may use the Irish figure of speech called a bull) will be a *ride*. A very dear friend has beguiled me into accompanying her in her pretty equipage to her beautiful home, four miles off; and having sent forward in the style of a running footman the servant who had driven her, she assumes the reins, and off we set.

My fair companion is a person whom nature and fortune would have spoiled if they could. She is one of those striking women whom a stranger cannot pass without turning to look again; tall and finely proportioned, with a bold Roman contour of figure and feature, a delicate English complexion, and an air of distinction altogether her own. Her beauty is duchess-like. She seems born to wear feathers and diamonds, and to form the grace and ornament of a court; and the noble frankness and simplicity of her countenance and manner confirm the impression. Destiny has, however, dealt more kindly by her. She is the wife of a rich country gentleman of high descent and higher attainments, to whom she is most devotedly attached; the mother of a little girl as lovely as herself, and the delight of all who have the happiness of her acquaintance, to whom she is endeared not merely by her remarkable sweetness of temper and kindness of heart, but by the singular ingenuousness and openness of character which communicate an indescribable charm to her conversation. She is as transparent as water. You may see every colour, every shade of a mind as lofty and beautiful as her person. Talking with her is like being in the Palace

of Truth described by Madame de Genlis; and yet so kindly
are her feelings, so great her indulgence to the little failings and
foibles of our common nature, so intense her sympathy with the
wants, the wishes, the sorrows, and the happiness of her fellow-
creatures, that, with all her frank speaking, I never knew her
make an enemy or lose a friend.

But we must get on. What would she say if she knew I was
putting her into print? We must get on up the hill. Ah! that
is precisely what we are not likely to do! This horse, this
beautiful and high-bred horse, well fed, and fat and glossy, who
stood prancing at our gate like an Arabian, has suddenly turned
sulky. He does not indeed stand quite still, but his way of moving is little better—the slowest and most sullen of all walks.
Even they who ply the hearse at funerals, sad-looking beasts
who totter under black feathers, go faster. It is of no use to
admonish him by whip, or rein, or word. The rogue has found
out, that it is a weak and tender hand that guides him now.
Oh, for one pull, one stroke of his old driver the groom! How
he would fly! But there is the groom half-a-mile before us, out
of ear-shot, clearing the ground at a capital rate, beating us
hollow. He has just turned the top of the hill; and in a moment
—ay, *now* he is out of sight, and will undoubtedly so continue
till he meets us at the lawn gate. Well! there is no great harm.
It is only prolonging the pleasure of enjoying together this
charming scenery in this fine weather. If once we make up our
minds not to care how slowly our steed goes, not to fret ourselves
by vain exertions, it is no matter what his pace may be. There
is little doubt of his getting home by sunset, and that will content us. He is, after all, a fine noble animal; and perhaps
when he finds that we are determined to give him his way,
he may relent and give us ours. All his sex are sticklers for
dominion, though, when it is undisputed, some of them are
generous enough to abandon it. Two or three of the most
discreet wives of my acquaintance contrive to manage their
husbands sufficiently with no better secret than this seeming
submission; and in our case the example has the more weight
since we have no possible way of helping ourselves.

Thus philosophizing, we reached the top of the hill, and
viewed with " reverted eyes " the beautiful prospect that lay
bathed in golden sunshine behind us. Cowper says, with that
boldness of expressing in poetry the commonest and simplest

feelings, which is perhaps one great secret of his originality,

> Scenes must be beautiful, which, daily seen,
> Please daily, and whose novelty survives
> Long knowledge and the scrutiny of years.

Every day I walk up this hill—every day I pause at the top to admire the broad winding road with the green waste on each side, uniting it with the thickly timbered hedgerows; the two pretty cottages at unequal distances, placed so as to mark the bends; the village beyond, with its mass of roofs and clustered chimneys peeping through the trees; and the rich distance, where cottages, mansions, churches, towns, seem embowered in some wide forest, and shut in by blue shadowy hills. Every day I admire this most beautiful landscape; yet never did it seem to me so fine or so glowing as now. All the tints of the glorious autumn, orange, tawny, yellow, red, are poured in profusion among the bright greens of the meadows and turnip fields, till the eyes are satiated with colour; and then before us we have the common with its picturesque roughness of surface tufted with cottages, dappled with water, edging off on one side into fields and farms and orchards, and terminated on the other by the princely oak avenue. What a richness and variety the wild broken ground gives to the luxuriant cultivation of the rest of the landscape! Cowper has described it for me. How perpetually, as we walk in the country, his vivid pictures recur to the memory! Here is his common and mine!

> The common overgrown with fern, and rough
> With prickly gorse, that, shapeless and deform'd
> And dangerous to the touch, has yet its bloom,
> And decks itself with ornaments of gold ;
> . . . there the turf
> Smells fresh, and, rich in odoriferous herbs
> And fungous fruits of earth, regales the sense
> With luxury of unexpected sweets.

The description is exact. There, too, to the left is my cricket-ground (Cowper's common wanted that finishing grace); and there stands one solitary urchin, as if in contemplation of its past and future glories; for, alas! cricket is over for the season. Ah! it is Ben Kirby, next brother to Joe, king of the youngsters, and probably his successor—for this Michaelmas has cost us Joe! He is promoted from the farm to the mansion-house, two miles off; there he cleans shoes, rubs knives, and runs on errands, and is, as his mother expresses it, " a sort of 'prentice to the footman." I should not wonder if Joe, some day or other, should overtop the footman, and rise to be butler; and his splendid prospects must be our consolation for the loss of this great favourite. In the meantime we have Ben.

Ben Kirby is a year younger than Joe, and the schoolfellow and rival of Jem Eusden. To be sure his abilities lie in rather a different line: Jem is a scholar, Ben is a wag: Jem is great in figures and writing, Ben in faces and mischief. His master says of him, that, if there were two such in the school, he must resign his office; and, as far as my observation goes, the worthy pedagogue is right. Ben is, it must be confessed, a great corrupter of gravity. He hath an exceeding aversion to authority and decorum, and a wonderful boldness and dexterity in overthrowing the one and puzzling the other. His contortions of visage are astounding. His " power over his own muscles and those of other people " is almost equal to that of Liston; and indeed the original face, flat and square and Chinese in its shape, of a fine tan complexion, with a snub nose, and a slit for a mouth, is nearly as comical as that matchless performer's. When aided by Ben's singular mobility of feature, his knowing winks and grins and shrugs and nods, together with a certain dry shrewdness, a habit of saying sharp things, and a marvellous gift of impudence, it forms as fine a specimen as possible of a humorous country boy, an oddity in embryo. Everybody likes Ben, except his butts (which may perhaps comprise half his acquaintance); and of them no one so thoroughly hates and dreads him as our parish schoolmaster, a most worthy King Log, whom Ben dumbfounds twenty times a day. He is a great ornament of the cricket-ground, has a real genius for the game, and displays it after a very original manner, under the disguise of awkwardness—as the clown shows off his agility in a pantomime. Nothing comes amiss to him. By the bye, he would have been the very lad for us in our present dilemma; not a horse in England could master Ben Kirby. But we are too far from him now—and perhaps it is as well that we are so. I believe the rogue has a kindness for me, in remembrance of certain apples and nuts, which my usual companion, who delights in his wit, is accustomed to dole out to him. But it is a Robin Goodfellow nevertheless, a perfect Puck, that loves nothing on earth so well as mischief. Perhaps the horse may be the safer conductor of the two.

The avenue is quite alive to-day. Old women are picking up twigs and acorns, and pigs of all sizes doing their utmost to spare them the latter part of the trouble; boys and girls groping for beech-nuts under yonder clump; and a group of younger elves collecting as many dead leaves as they can find to feed the bonfire which is smoking away so briskly amongst the trees—a sort of rehearsal of the grand bonfire nine days hence; of the loyal conflagration of the arch traitor Guy Vaux, which is annually solemnized in the avenue, accompanied with as much of squibbery and crackery as our boys can beg or borrow—not to say steal. Ben Kirby is a great man on the 5th of November. All the savings of a month, the hoarded halfpence, the new farthings, the very luck-penny, go off *in fumo* on that night. For my part, I like this day-light mockery better. There is no gunpowder—odious gunpowder! no noise but the merry shouts of the small fry, so shrill and happy, and the cawing of the rooks, who are wheeling in large circles overhead, and wondering what is going forward in their territory—seeming in their loud clamour to ask what that light smoke may mean that curls so prettily amongst their old oaks, towering as if to meet the clouds. There is something very intelligent in the ways of that black people the rooks, particularly in their wonder. I suppose it results from their numbers and their unity of purpose, a sort of collective and corporate wisdom. Yet geese congregate also; and geese never by any chance look wise. But then geese are a domestic fowl; we have spoiled them; and rooks are free commoners of nature, who use the habitations we provide for them, tenant our groves and our avenues, but never dream of becoming our subjects.

What a labyrinth of a road this is! I do think there are four turnings in the short half-mile between the avenue and the mill. And what a pity, as my companion observes—not that our good and jolly miller, the very representative of the Old English yeomanry, should be so rich, but that one consequence of his riches should be the pulling down of the prettiest old mill that ever looked at itself in the Loddon, with the picturesque, low-browed, irregular cottage, which stood with its light-pointed roof, its clustered chimneys, and its ever-open door, looking like the real abode of comfort and hospitality, to build this huge, staring, frightful, red-brick mill, as ugly as a manufactory, and this great square house, ugly and red to match, just behind.

The old buildings always used to remind me of Wollett's beautiful engraving of a scene in the Maid of the Mill. It will be long before any artist will make a drawing of this. Only think of this redness in a picture! this boiled lobster of a house! Falstaff's description of Bardolph's nose would look pale in the comparison.

Here is that monstrous machine of a tilted waggon, with its load of flour, and its four fat horses. I wonder whether our horse will have the decency to get out of the way. If he does

not, I am sure we cannot make him; and that enormous ship upon wheels, that ark on dry land, would roll over us like the car of Juggernaut. Really—Oh no! there is no danger now. I should have remembered that it is my friend Samuel Long who drives the mill-team. He will take care of us. " Thank you, Samuel! " And Samuel has put us on our way, steered us safely past his waggon, escorted us over the bridge; and now, having seen us through our immediate difficulties, has parted from us with a very civil bow and good-humoured smile, as one who is always civil and good-humoured, but with a certain triumphant masterful look in his eyes, which I have noted in men, even the best of them, when a woman gets into straits by attempting manly employments. He has done us great good though, and

may be allowed his little feeling of superiority. The parting
salute he bestowed on our steed, in the shape of an astounding
crack of his huge whip, has put that refractory animal on his
mettle. On we go! past the glazier's pretty house, with its
porch and its filbert walk; along the narrow lane bordered with
elms, whose fallen leaves have made the road one yellow; past
that little farm-house with the horse-chestnut trees before, glowing like oranges; past the whitewashed school on the other
side, gay with October roses; past the park, and the lodge, and
the mansion, where once dwelt the great earl of Clarendon;
and now the rascal has begun to discover that Samuel Long and
his whip are a mile off, and that his mistress is driving him, and
he slackens his pace accordingly. Perhaps he feels the beauty
of the road just here, and goes slowly to enjoy it. Very beautiful
it certainly is. The park paling forms the boundary on one side,
with fine clumps of oak, and deer in all attitudes; the water,
tufted with alders, flowing along on the other. Another turn,
and the water winds away, succeeded by a low hedge, and a
sweep of green meadows: whilst the park and its paling are
replaced by a steep bank, on which stands a small, quiet village
alehouse; and higher up, embosomed in wood, is the little
country church, with its sloping churchyard and its low white
steeple, peeping out from amongst magnificent yew-trees:

> Huge trunks ! and each particular trunk a growth
> Of intertwisted fibres serpentine
> Up-coiling, and invet'rately convolved.
> 　　　　　　　　　　　　　　　WORDSWORTH

No village church was ever more happily placed. It is the very
image of the peace and humbleness inculcated within its walls.

Ah! here is a higher hill rising before us, almost like a mountain. How grandly the view opens as we ascend over that wild
bank, overgrown with fern, and heath, and gorse, and between
those tall hollies, glowing with their coral berries! What an
expanse! But we have little time to gaze at present; for that
piece of perversity, our horse, who has walked over so much
level ground, has now, inspired, I presume, by a desire to revisit
his stable, taken it into that unaccountable noddle of his to trot
up this, the very steepest hill in the county. Here we are on the
top; and in five minutes we have reached the lawn gate, and are
in the very midst of that beautiful piece of art or nature (I do
not know to which class it belongs), the pleasure-ground of

F. Hill. Never was the " prophetic eye of taste " exerted with more magical skill than in these plantations. Thirty years ago this place had no existence; it was a mere undistinguished tract of field and meadow and common land; now it is a mimic forest, delighting the eye with the finest combinations of trees and shrubs, the rarest effects of form and foliage, and bewildering the mind with its green glades, and impervious recesses, and apparently interminable extent. It is the triumph of landscape gardening, and never more beautiful than in this autumn sunset, lighting up the ruddy beech and the spotted sycamore, and gilding the shining fir-cones that hang so thickly amongst the dark pines. The robins are singing around us, as if they too felt the magic of the hour. How gracefully the road winds through the leafy labyrinth, leading imperceptibly to the more ornamented sweep. Here we are at the door amidst geraniums, and carnations, and jasmines, still in flower. Ah! here is a flower sweeter than all, a bird gayer than the robin, the little bird that chirps to the tune of " mamma! mamma! " the bright-faced fairy, whose tiny feet come pattering along, making a merry music, mamma's own Frances! And following her guidance, here we are in the dear round room time enough to catch the last rays of the sun, as they light the noble landscape which lies like a panorama around us, lingering longest on that long island of old thorns and stunted oaks, the oasis of B. Heath, and then vanishing in a succession of gorgeous clouds.

October 28th.—Another soft and brilliant morning. But the pleasures of to-day must be written in short-hand. I have left myself no room for notes of admiration.

First we drove about the coppice: an extensive wood of oak, and elm, and beech, chiefly the former, which adjoins the park paling of F. Hill, of which demesne, indeed, it forms one of the most delightful parts. The roads through the coppice are studiously wild; so that they have the appearance of mere cart-tracks: and the manner in which the ground is tumbled about, the steep declivities, the sunny slopes, the sudden swells and falls, now a close narrow valley, then a sharp ascent to an eminence commanding an immense extent of prospect, have a striking air of natural beauty, developed and heightened by the perfection of art. All this, indeed, was familiar to me; the colouring only was new. I had been there in early spring, when the fragrant palms were on the willow, and the yellow tassels on the hazel, and every twig was swelling with renewed life; and I had been there again and again in the green leafiness of midsummer; but never as now, when the dark verdure of the fir plantations, hanging over the picturesque and unequal paling, partly covered with moss and ivy, contrasts so remarkably with the shining orange-leaves of the beech, already half fallen, the pale yellow of the scattering elm, the deeper and richer tints of the oak, and the glossy stems of the " lady of the woods," the delicate weeping birch. The underwood is no less picturesque. The red-spotted leaves and redder berries of the old thorns, the scarlet festoons of the bramble, the tall fern of every hue, seem to vie with the brilliant mosaic of the ground, now covered with dead leaves and strewn with fir-cones, now, where a little glade intervenes, gay with various mosses and splendid *fungi*. How beautiful is this coppice to-day! especially where the little spring, as clear as crystal, comes bubbling out from the " old fantastic " beech root, and trickles over the grass, bright and silent as the dew in a May morning. The wood-pigeons (who are just returned from their summer migration, and are cropping the ivy berries) add their low cooings, the very note of love, to the slight fluttering of the falling leaves in the quiet air, giving a voice to the sunshine and the beauty. This coppice is a place to live and die in. But we must go. And how fine is the ascent which leads us again into the world, past those cottages hidden as in a pit, and by that hanging orchard and that rough heathy bank! The scenery in this one spot has a wildness, an abruptness of rise and fall, rare in any part of England, rare above all in this rich and lovely but monotonous county. It is Switzerland in miniature.

And now we cross the hill to pay a morning visit to the family at the great house—another fine place, commanding another fine sweep of country. The park, studded with old trees, and sinking gently into a valley, rich in wood and water, is in the best style of ornamental landscape, though more according to the common routine of gentlemen's seats than the singularly original place which we have just left. There is, however, one distinctive beauty in the grounds of the great house—the magnificent firs which shade the terraces and surround the sweep, giving out in summer odours really Sabæan, and now in this low autumn sun producing an effect almost magical, as the huge red trunks, garlanded with ivy, stand out from the deep shadows like an army of giants. Indoors—Oh I must not take my readers indoors, or we shall never get away!—Indoors the sunshine is brighter still; for there, in a lofty lightsome room, sat a damsel fair and arch and *piquant*, one whom Titian or Velasquez should be born again to paint, leaning over an instrument [1] as sparkling and fanciful as herself, singing pretty French romances, and Scottish Jacobite songs, and all sorts of graceful and airy drolleries picked up I know not where—an English improvisatrice! a gayer Annot Lyle! whilst her sister, of a higher order of beauty, and with an earnest kindness in her smile that deepens its power, lends to the piano, as her father to the violin, an expression, a sensibility, a spirit, an eloquence almost superhuman—almost divine! Oh to hear these two instruments accompanying my dear companion (I forgot to say that she is a singer worthy to be so accompanied) in Haydn's exquisite canzonet, *She never told her love*—to hear her voice, with all its power, its sweetness, its gush of sound, so sustained and assisted by modulations that rivalled its intensity of expression; to hear at once such poetry, such music, such execution, is a pleasure never to be forgotten, or mixed with meaner things. I seem to hear it still.

> As in the bursting spring time o'er the eye
>   Of one who haunts the fields fair visions creep
>   Beneath the closed lids (afore dull sleep
> Dims the quick fancy) of sweet flowers that lie
> On grassy banks, oxlip of orient dye,
>   And palest primrose and blue violet,
>   All in their fresh and dewy beauty set,
> Pictured within the sense, and will not fly :
> So in mine ear resounds and lives again
>   One mingled melody—a voice, a pair
>   Of instruments most voice-like ! Of the air
> Rather than of the earth seems that high strain,
> A spirit's song, and worthy of the train
>   That soothed old Prospero with music rare.

[1] The dital harp.

THE COPSE

APRIL 18TH.—Sad wintry weather; a north-east wind; a sun that puts out one's eyes, without affording the slightest warmth; dryness that chaps lips and hands like a frost in December; rain that comes chilling and arrowy like hail in January; nature at a dead pause; no seeds up in the garden; no leaves out in the hedgerows; no cowslips swinging their pretty bells in the fields; no nightingales in the dingles; no swallows skimming round the great pond; no cuckoos (that ever I should miss that rascally sonneteer!) in any part. Nevertheless there is something of a charm in this wintry spring, this putting-back of the seasons. If the flower-clock must stand still for a month or two, could it choose a better time than that of the primroses and violets? I never remember (and for such gauds my memory, if not very good for aught of wise or useful, may be trusted) such an affluence of the one or such a duration of the other. Primrosy is the epithet which this year will retain in my recollection. Hedge, ditch, meadow, field, even the very paths and highways, are set with them; but their chief *habitat* is a certain copse, about a mile off, where they are spread like a carpet, and where I go to visit them rather oftener than quite comports with the dignity of a lady of mature age. I am going thither this very afternoon, and May and her company are going too.

This Mayflower of mine is a strange animal. Instinct and imitation make in her an approach to reason which is sometimes almost startling. She mimics all that she sees us do, with the dexterity of a monkey, and far more of gravity and apparent purpose; cracks nuts and eats them; gathers currants and severs them from the stalk with the most delicate nicety; filches and munches apples and pears; is as dangerous in an orchard as a schoolboy; smells to flowers; smiles at meeting; answers in a pretty lively voice when spoken to (sad pity that the language should be unknown!), and has greatly the advantage of us in a conversation, inasmuch as our meaning is certainly clear to her; all this and a thousand amusing prettinesses (to say nothing of her canine feat of bringing her game straight to her master's feet, and refusing to resign it to any hand but his) does my beautiful greyhound perform untaught, by the mere effect of imitation and sagacity. Well, May, at the end of the coursing season, having lost Brush, our old spaniel, her great friend, and the blue greyhound Mariette, her comrade and rival, both of which four-footed worthies were sent out to keep for the summer, began to find solitude a weary condition, and to look abroad for company. Now it so happened that the same suspension of sport which had reduced our little establishment from three dogs to one, had also dispersed the splendid kennel of a celebrated courser in our neighbourhood, three of whose finest young dogs came home to " their walk " (as the sporting phrase goes) at the collar-maker's in our village. May, accordingly, on the first morning of her solitude (she had never taken the slightest notice of her neighbours before, although they had sojourned in our street upwards of a fortnight) bethought herself of the timely resource offered to her by the vicinity of these canine *beaux*, and went up boldly and knocked at their stable door, which was already very commodiously on the half-latch. The three dogs came out with much alertness and gallantry, and May, declining apparently to enter their territories, brought them off to her own. This manœuvre has been repeated every day, with one variation; of the three dogs, the first a brindle, the second a yellow, and the third a black, the two first only are now admitted to walk or consort with her, and the last, poor fellow, for no fault that I can discover except May's caprice, is driven away not only by the fair lady, but even by his old companions —is, so to say, sent to Coventry. Of her two permitted followers, the yellow gentleman, Saladin by name, is decidedly the favourite. He is, indeed, May's shadow, and will walk with me whether I choose or not. It is quite impossible to get rid of him unless by discarding Miss May also; and to accomplish a walk in the country without her would be like an adventure of Don Quixote without his faithful 'squire Sancho.

So forth we set, May and I, and Saladin and the brindle; May and myself walking with the sedateness and decorum befitting our sex and age (she is five years old this grass, rising six) —the young things, for the soldan and the brindle are (not meaning any disrespect) little better than puppies, frisking and frolicking as best pleased them.

Our route lay for the first part along the sheltered quiet lanes which lead to our old habitation; a way never trodden by me without peculiar and home-like feelings, full of the recollections, the pains and pleasures, of other days. But we are not to talk sentiment now—even May would not understand that maudlin language. We must get on. What a wintry hedgerow this is for the eighteenth of April! Primrosy to be sure, abundantly spangled with those stars of the earth—but so bare, so leafless, so cold! The wind whistles through the brown boughs as in winter. Even the early elder shoots, which do make an approach to springiness, look brown, and the small leaves of the woodbine, which have also ventured to peep forth, are of a sad purple, frost-bitten, like a dairymaid's elbows on a snowy morning. The very birds, in this season of pairing and building, look chilly and uncomfortable, and their nests!—" Oh Saladin! come away from the hedge! Don't you see that what puzzles you and makes you leap up in the air is a redbreast's nest? Don't you see the pretty speckled eggs? Don't you hear the poor hen calling as it were for help? Come here this moment, sir! " And by good luck Saladin (who for a paynim has tolerable qualities) comes, before he has touched the nest, or before his playmate the brindle, the less manageable of the two, has espied it.

Now we go round the corner and cross the bridge, where the common, with its clear stream winding between clumps of elms, assumes so park-like an appearance. Who is this approaching so slowly and majestically, this square bundle of petticoat and cloak, this road-waggon of a woman? It is, it must be Mrs Sally Mearing, the completest specimen within my knowledge of farmeresses (may I be allowed that innovation in language?) as they were. It can be nobody else.

Mrs Sally Mearing, when I first became acquainted with her, occupied, together with her father (a superannuated man of ninety), a large farm very near our former habitation. It had been anciently a great manor-farm or court-house, and was still a stately, substantial building, whose lofty halls and spacious chambers gave an air of grandeur to the common offices to which they were applied. Traces of gilding might yet be seen on the panels which covered the walls, and on the huge carved chimney-pieces which rose almost to the ceilings; and the marble tables and the inlaid oak staircase still spoke of the former grandeur of the court. Mrs Sally corresponded well with the date of her mansion, although she troubled herself little with its dignity. She was thoroughly of the old school, and had a most comfortable contempt for the new: rose at four in winter and summer, breakfasted at six, dined at eleven in the forenoon, supped at five, and was regularly in bed before eight, except when the hay-time or the harvest imperiously required her to sit up till sunset,—a necessity to which she submitted with no very good grace. To a deviation from these hours, and to the modern iniquities of white aprons, cotton stockings, and muslin handkerchiefs (Mrs Sally herself always wore check, black worsted, and a sort of yellow compound which she was wont to call *susy*), together with the invention of drill plough and thrashing machines and other agricultural novelties, she failed not to attribute all the mishaps or misdoings of the whole parish. The last-mentioned discovery especially aroused her indignation. Oh to hear her descant on the merits of the flail, wielded by a stout right arm, such as she had known in her youth (for by her account there was as great a deterioration in bones and sinews as in the other implements of husbandry), was enough to make the very inventor break his machine. She would even take up her favourite instrument and thrash the air herself by way of illustrating her argument, and, to say truth, few men in these degenerate days could have matched the stout, brawny, muscular limb which Mrs Sally displayed at sixty-five.

In spite of this contumacious rejection of agricultural improvements, the world went well with her at Court-Farm. A good landlord, an easy rent, incessant labour, unremitting frugality, and excellent times, insured a regular though moderate profit: and she lived on, grumbling and prospering, flourishing and complaining, till two misfortunes befell her at once—her father died, and her lease expired. The loss of her father, although a bedridden man, turned of ninety, who could not in the course of nature have been expected to live long, was a terrible shock to a daughter who was not so much younger as to be without fears for her own life, and who had besides been so used to nursing the good old man, and looking to his little comforts, that she missed him as a mother would miss an ailing child. The expiration of the lease was a grievance and a puzzle of a different nature. Her landlord would have willingly retained his excellent tenant, but not on the terms on which she then held the land, which had not varied for fifty years: so that poor Mrs Sally had the misfortune to find rent rising and prices sinking both at the same moment—a terrible solecism in political

F

economy. Even this, however, I believe she would have endured, rather than have quitted the house where she was born,
and to which all her ways and notions were adapted, had not a
priggish steward, as much addicted to improvement and reform
as she was to precedent and established usages, insisted on bind-
ing her by lease to spread a certain number of loads of chalk on
every field. This tremendous innovation, for never had that
novelty in manure whitened the crofts and pightles of Court-
Farm, decided her at once. She threw the proposals into the
fire and left the place in a week.

Her choice of a habitation occasioned some wonder, and
much amusement in our village world. To be sure, upon the
verge of seventy, an old maid may be permitted to dispense with
the more rigid punctilio of her class, but Mrs Sally had always
been so tenacious on the score of character, so very a prude, so
determined an avoider of the " men folk " (as she was wont
contemptuously to call them) that we all were conscious of
something like astonishment, on finding that she and her little
handmaid had taken up their abode in one end of a spacious
farm-house belonging to the bluff old bachelor, George Robinson, of the Lea. Now farmer Robinson was quite as notorious
for his aversion to petticoated things as Mrs Sally for her hatred
to the unfeathered bipeds who wear doublet and hose, so that
there was a little astonishment in that quarter too, and plenty
of jests, which the honest farmer speedily silenced, by telling all
who joked on the subject that he had given his lodger fair
warning, that, let people say what they would, he was quite
determined not to marry her; so that if she had any views that
way, it would be better for her to go elsewhere. This declara-
tion, which must be admitted to have been more remarkable
for frankness than civility, made, however, no ill impression on
Mrs Sally. To the farmer's she went, and at his house she lives
still, with her little maid, her tabby cat, a decrepit sheep-dog,
and much of the lumber of Court-Farm, which she could not
find in her heart to part from. There she follows her old ways
and her old hours, untempted by matrimony, and unassailed
(as far as I hear) by love or by scandal, with no other grievance
than an occasional dearth of employment for herself and her
young lass (even pewter dishes do not always want scouring),
and now and then a twinge of the rheumatism.

Here she is, that good relique of the olden time—for, in spite of her whims and prejudices, a better and a kinder woman never lived—here she is, with the hood of her red cloak pulled over her close black bonnet, of that silk which once (it may be presumed) was fashionable, since it is still called mode, and her whole stout figure huddled up in a miscellaneous and most substantial covering of thick petticoats, gowns, aprons, shawls, and cloaks—a weight which it requires the strength of a thrasher to walk under—here she is, with her square honest visage, and her loud frank voice; and we hold a pleasant disjointed chat of rheumatisms and early chickens, bad weather, and hats with feathers in them—the last exceedingly sore subject being introduced by poor Jane Davis (a cousin of Mrs Sally), who, passing us in a beaver bonnet, on her road from school, stopped to drop her little curtsy, and was soundly scolded for her civility. Jane, who is a gentle, humble, smiling lass, about twelve years old, receives so many rebukes from her worthy relative, and bears them so meekly, that I should not wonder if they were to be followed by a legacy: I sincerely wish they may. Well, at last we said good-bye; when, on inquiring my destination, and hearing that I was bent to the ten-acre copse (part of the farm which she ruled so long), she stopped me to tell a dismal story of two sheep-stealers who, sixty years ago, were found hidden in that copse, and only taken after great difficulty and resistance, and the maiming of a peace-officer.—" Pray don't go there, Miss! For mercy's sake don't be so venturesome! Think if they should kill you! " were the last words of Mrs Sally.

Many thanks for her care and kindness! But, without being at all foolhardy in general, I have no great fear of the sheep-stealers of sixty years ago. Even if they escaped hanging for that exploit, I should greatly doubt their being in case to attempt another. So on we go: down the short shady lane, and out on the pretty retired green, shut in by fields and hedgerows, which we must cross to reach the copse. How lively this green nook is to-day, half covered with cows, and horses, and sheep! And how glad these frolicsome greyhounds are to exchange the hard gravel of the high road for this pleasant short turf, which seems made for their gambols! How beautifully they are at play, chasing each other round and round in lessening circles, darting off at all kinds of angles, crossing and recrossing May, and trying to win her sedateness into a game at romps, turning round on each other with gay defiance, pursuing the cows and the colts, leaping up as if to catch the crows in their flight—all in their harmless and innocent—" Ah wretches! villains! rascals! four-footed mischiefs! canine plagues! Saladin! Brindle! "— They are after the sheep—" Saladin, I say! "—They have actually singled out that pretty spotted lamb—" Brutes, if I catch you! Saladin! Brindle! " We shall be taken up for sheep-stealing presently ourselves. They have chased the poor little lamb into a ditch, and are mounting guard over it, standing at bay.—" Ah wretches, I have you now! for shame, Saladin! Get away, Brindle! See how good May is. Off with you, brutes! For shame! For shame! " and brandishing a handkerchief, which could hardly be an efficient instrument of correction, I succeeded in driving away the two puppies, who after all meant nothing more than play, although it was somewhat rough, and rather too much in the style of the old fable of the boys and the frogs. May is gone after them, perhaps to scold them : for she has been as grave as a judge during the whole proceeding, keeping ostentatiously close to me, and taking no part whatever in the mischief.

The poor little pretty lamb! here it lies on the bank quite motionless, frightened I believe to death, for certainly those villains never touched it. It does not stir. Does it breathe? Oh yes, it does! It is alive, safe enough. Look, it opens its eyes, and, finding the coast clear and its enemies far away, it springs up in a moment and gallops to its dam, who has stood bleating the whole time at a most respectful distance. Who would suspect a lamb of so much simple cunning? I really thought the pretty thing was dead—and now how glad the ewe is to recover her curling spotted little one! How fluttered they look! Well! this adventure has flurried me too ; between fright and running, I warrant you my heart beats as fast as the lamb's.

Ah! here is the shameless villain Saladin, the cause of the commotion, thrusting his slender nose into my hand to beg pardon and make up! " Oh wickedest of soldans! Most iniquitous pagan! Soul of a Turk! "—but there is no resisting the good-humoured creature's penitence. I must pat him. "There! there! Now we will go to the copse, I am sure we shall find no worse malefactors than ourselves—shall we, May?—and the sooner we get out of sight of the sheep the better ; for Brindle seems meditating another attack. *Allons, messieurs*, over this gate, across this meadow, and here is the copse."

How boldly that superb ash-tree with its fine silver bark rises from the bank, and what a fine entrance it makes with the holly beside it, which also deserves to be called a tree! But here we are in the copse. Ah! only one half of the underwood was cut last year, and the other is at its full growth: hazel, brier, woodbine, bramble, forming one impenetrable thicket, and almost uniting with the lower branches of the elms, and oaks, and beeches, which rise at regular distances overhead. No foot can penetrate that dense and thorny entanglement; but there is a walk all round by the side of the wide sloping bank, walk and bank and copse carpeted with primroses, whose fresh and balmy odour impregnates the very air. Oh how exquisitely beautiful! and it is not the primroses only, those gems of flowers, but the natural mosaic of which they form a part: that network of ground-ivy, with its lilac blossoms and the subdued tint of its purplish leaves, those rich mosses, those enamelled wild hyacinths, those spotted arums, and above all those wreaths of ivy linking all those flowers together with chains of leaves more beautiful than blossoms, whose white veins seem swelling amidst the deep green or splendid brown;—it is the whole earth that is so beautiful! Never surely were primroses so richly set, and never did primroses better deserve such a setting. There they are of their own lovely yellow, the hue to which they have given a name, the exact tint of the butterfly that overhangs them (the first I have seen this year! can spring really be coming at last?) —sprinkled here and there with tufts of a reddish purple, and others of the purest white, as some accident of soil affects that strange and inscrutable operation of nature, the colouring of flowers. Oh how fragrant they are, and how pleasant it is to sit in this sheltered copse, listening to the fine creaking of the wind amongst the branches, the most unearthly of sounds, with this gay tapestry under our feet, and the wood-pigeons flitting from tree to tree, and mixing the deep note of love with the elemental music.

Yes! spring is coming. Wood-pigeons, butterflies, and sweet flowers, all give token of the sweetest of the seasons. Spring is coming. The hazel stalks are swelling and putting forth their pale tassels, the satin palms with their honeyed odours are out on the willow, and the last lingering winter berries are dropping from the hawthorn, and making way for the bright and blossomy leaves.

THE WOOD

APRIL 20TH.—Spring is actually come now, with the fulness and almost the suddenness of a northern summer. To-day is completely April—clouds and sunshine, wind and showers; blossoms on the trees, grass in the fields, swallows by the ponds, snakes in the hedgerows, nightingales in the thickets, and cuckoos everywhere. My young friend Ellen G. is going with me this evening to gather wood-sorrel. She never saw that most elegant plant, and is so delicate an artist that the introduction will be a mutual benefit; Ellen will gain a subject worthy of her pencil, and the pretty weed will live—no small favour to a flower almost as transitory as the gum cistus: duration is the only charm which it wants, and that Ellen will give it. The weather is, to be sure, a little threatening, but we are not people to mind the weather when we have an object in view; we shall certainly go in quest of the wood-sorrel, and will take May, provided we can escape May's followers; for since the adventure of the lamb, Saladin has had an affair with a gander, furious in defence of his goslings, in which rencontre the gander came off conqueror; and as geese abound in the wood to which we are going (called by the country people the Pinge), and the victory may not always incline to the right side, I should be very sorry to lead the Soldan to fight his battles over again. We will take nobody but May.

So saying, we proceeded on our way through winding lanes, between hedgerows tenderly green, till we reached the hatchgate, with the white cottage beside it embossomed in fruit-trees, which forms the entrance to the Pinge, and in a moment the whole scene was before our eyes.

" Is not this beautiful, Ellen ? " The answer could hardly be other than a glowing rapid " Yes! "—A wood is generally a pretty place; but this wood—Imagine a smaller forest, full of glades and sheep-walks, surrounded by irregular cottages with their blooming orchards, a clear stream winding about the brakes, and a road intersecting it, and giving life and light to the picture; and you will have a faint idea of the Pinge. Every step was opening a new point of view, a fresh combination of glade and path and thicket. The accessories too were changing every moment. Ducks, geese, pigs, and children, giving way, as we advanced into the wood, to sheep and forest ponies; and they again disappearing as we became more entangled in its mazes, till we heard nothing but the song of the nightingale, and saw only the silent flowers.

What a piece of fairy land! The tall elms overhead just bursting into tender vivid leaf, with here and there a hoary oak or a silver-barked beech, every twig swelling with the brown buds, and yet not quite stripped of the tawny foliage of autumn; tall hollies and hawthorn beneath, with their crisp brilliant leaves mixed with the white blossoms of the sloe, and woven together with garlands of woodbines and wild-briers; what a fairy land!

Primroses, cowslips, pansies, and the regular open-eyed white blossom of the wood anemone (or to use the more elegant Hampshire name, the windflower), were set under our feet as thick as daisies in a meadow; but the pretty weed that we came to seek was coyer; and Ellen began to fear that we had mistaken the place or the season.—At last she had herself the pleasure of finding it under a brake of holly—" Oh look! look! I am sure that this is the wood-sorrel! Look at the pendent white flower, shaped like a snowdrop and veined with purple streaks, and the beautiful trefoil leaves folded like a heart—some, the young ones, so vividly yet tenderly green that the foliage of the elm and the hawthorn would show dully at their side—others of a deeper tint, and lined, as it were, with a rich and changeful purple!—Don't you see them? " pursued my dear young friend, who is a delightful piece of life and sunshine, and was half inclined to scold me for the calmness with which, amused by her enthusiasm, I stood listening to her ardent exclamations—" Don't you see them? Oh how beautiful! and in what quantity! what profusion! See how the dark shade of the holly sets off the light and delicate colouring of the flower!— And see that other bed of them springing from the rich moss in the roots of that old beech-tree! Pray let us gather some. Here are baskets." So, quickly and carefully we began gathering, leaves, blossoms, roots and all, for the plant is so fragile that it will not brook separation; quickly and carefully we gathered, encountering divers petty misfortunes in spite of all our care, now caught by the veil in a holly bush, now hitching our shawls in a bramble, still gathering on, in spite of scratched fingers, till we had nearly filled our baskets and began to talk of our departure—

" But where is May? May! May! No going home without her. May! Here she comes galloping, the beauty! "—(Ellen is almost as fond of May as I am.)—" What has she got in her mouth? that rough, round, brown substance which she touches so tenderly? What can it be? A bird's nest? Naughty May! "

" No! as I live, a hedgehog! Look, Ellen, how it has coiled itself into a thorny ball! Off with it, May! Don't bring it to me! "—And May, somewhat reluctant to part with her prickly prize, however troublesome of carriage, whose change of shape seemed to me to have puzzled her sagacity more than any event I ever witnessed, for in general she has perfectly the air of understanding all that is going forward—May at last dropt the hedgehog; continuing, however, to pat it with her delicate cat-like paw, cautiously and daintily applied, and caught back suddenly

and rapidly after every touch, as if her poor captive had been a
red-hot coal. Finding that these pats entirely failed in solving
the riddle (for the hedgehog shammed dead, like the lamb the
other day, and appeared entirely motionless), she gave him so
spirited a nudge with her pretty black nose, that she not only
turned him over, but sent him rolling some little way along the
turfy path—an operation which that sagacious quadruped endured with the most perfect passiveness, the most admirable
non-resistance. No wonder that May's discernment was at
fault; I myself, if I had not been aware of the trick, should
have said that the ugly rough thing which she was trundling
along, like a bowl or a cricket-ball, was an inanimate substance,
something devoid of sensation and of will. At last my poor pet,
thoroughly perplexed and tired out, fairly relinquished the
contest, and came slowly away, turning back once or twice to
look at the object of her curiosity, as if half inclined to return
and try the event of another shove. The sudden flight of a
wood-pigeon effectually diverted her attention; and Ellen
amused herself by fancying how the hedgehog was scuttling
away, till our notice was also attracted by a very different object.

We had nearly threaded the wood, and were approaching an
open grove of magnificent oaks on the other side, when sounds
other than of nightingales burst on our ear, the deep and frequent strokes of the woodman's axe, and emerging from the
Pinge we discovered the havoc which that axe had committed.
Above twenty of the finest trees lay stretched on the velvet turf.
There they lay in every shape and form of devastation: some,
bare trunks stripped ready for the timber carriage, with the
bark built up in long piles at the side; some with the spoilers
busy about them, stripping, hacking, hewing; others with their
noble branches, their brown and fragrant shoots all fresh as if
they were alive—majestic corses, the slain of to-day! The grove
was like a field of battle. The young lads who were stripping
the bark, the very children who were picking up the chips,
seemed awed and silent, as if conscious that death was around
them. The nightingales sang faintly and interruptedly—a few
low frightened notes like a requiem.

Ah! here we are at the very scene of murder, the very tree
that they are felling; they have just hewn round the trunk with
those slaughtering axes, and are about to saw it asunder. After
all, it is a fine and thrilling operation, as the work of death

usually is. Into how grand an attitude was that young man thrown as he gave the final strokes round the root; and how wonderful is the effect of that supple and apparently powerless saw, bending like a riband, and yet overmastering that giant of the woods, conquering and overthrowing that thing of life! Now it has passed half through the trunk, and the woodman has begun to calculate which way the tree will fall; he drives a wedge to direct its course; now a few more movements of the noiseless saw; and then a larger wedge. See how the branches tremble! Hark how the trunk begins to crack! Another stroke of the huge hammer on the wedge, and the tree quivers, as with a mortal agony, shakes, reels, and falls. How slow, and solemn, and awful it is! How like to death, to human death in its grandest form! Cæsar in the Capitol, Seneca in the bath, could not fall more sublimely than that oak.

Even the heavens seem to sympathize with the devastation. The clouds have gathered into one thick low canopy, dark and vapoury as the smoke which overhangs London; the setting sun is just gleaming underneath with a dim and bloody glare, and the crimson rays spreading upward with a lurid and portentous grandeur, a subdued and dusky glow, like the light reflected on the sky from some vast conflagration. The deep flush fades away, and the rain begins to descend; and we hurry homeward rapidly, yet sadly, forgetful alike of the flowers, the hedgehog, and the wetting, thinking and talking only of the fallen tree.

THE DELL

M AY 2ND.—A delicious evening—bright sunshine; light
summer air; a sky almost cloudless; and a fresh yet
delicate verdure on the hedges and in the fields; an evening
that seems made for a visit to my newly discovered haunt, the
mossy dell, one of the most beautiful spots in the neighbourhood, which after passing, times out of number, the field which
it terminates, we found out about two months ago from the
accident of May's killing a rabbit there. May has had a fancy
for the place ever since; and so have I.

Thither accordingly we bend our way; through the village;
up the hill; along the common; past the avenue; across the
bridge; and by the mill. How deserted the road is to-night!
We have not seen a single acquaintance, except poor blind
Robert, laden with his sack of grass plucked from the hedges,
and the little boy that leads him. A singular division of labour!
Little Jem guides Robert to the spots where the long grass grows,
and tells him where it is most plentiful; and then the old man
cuts it close to the roots, and between them they fill the sack,
and sell the contents in the village. Half the cows in the street
—for our baker, our wheelwright, and our shoemaker has each
his Alderney—owe the best part of their maintenance to blind
Robert's industry.

Here we are at the entrance of the corn-field which leads to
the dell, and which commands so fine a view of the Loddon,
the mill, the great farm, with its picturesque outbuildings,
and the range of woody hills beyond. It is impossible not to
pause a moment at that gate, the landscape, always beautiful,
is so suited to the season and the hour—so bright, and gay, and
spring-like. But May, who has the chance of another rabbit in
her pretty head, has galloped forward to the dingle, and poor
May, who follows me so faithfully in all my wanderings, has a
right to a little indulgence in hers. So to the dingle we go.

At the end of the field, which when seen from the road seems
terminated by a thick dark coppice, we come suddenly to the
edge of a ravine, on one side fringed with a low growth of alder,
birch, and willow, on the other mossy, turfy, and bare, or only

broken by bright tufts of blossomed broom. One or two old pollards almost conceal the winding road that leads down the descent, by the side of which a spring as bright as crystal runs gurgling along. The dell itself is an irregular piece of broken ground, in some parts very deep, intersected by two or three high banks of equal irregularity, now abrupt and bare, and rock-like, now crowned with tufts of the feathery willow or magnificent old thorns. Everywhere the earth is covered by short fine turf, mixed with mosses, soft, beautiful, and various, and embossed with the speckled leaves and lilac flowers of the arum, the paler blossoms of the common orchis, the enamelled blue of the wild hyacinth, so splendid in this evening light, and large tufts of oxlips and cowslips rising like nosegays from the short turf.

The ground on the other side of the dell is much lower than the field through which we came, so that it is mainly to the labyrinthine intricacy of these high banks that it owes its singular character of wildness and variety. Now we seem hemmed in by those green cliffs, shut out from all the world, with nothing visible but those verdant mounds and the deep blue sky; now by some sudden turn we get a peep at an adjoining meadow, where the sheep are lying, dappling its sloping surface like the small clouds on the summer heaven. Poor harmless, quiet creatures, how still they are! Some socially lying side by side; some grouped in threes and fours; some quite apart. Ah! there are lambs amongst them—pretty, pretty lambs!—nestled in by their mothers. Soft, quiet, sleepy things! Not all so quiet, though! There is a party of these young lambs as wide awake as heart can desire; half a dozen of them playing together, frisking, dancing, leaping, butting, and crying in the young voice, which is so pretty a diminutive of the full-grown bleat. How beautiful they are with their innocent spotted faces, their mottled feet, their long curly tails, and their light flexible forms, frolicking like so many kittens, but with a gentleness, an assurance of sweetness and innocence, which no kitten, nothing that ever is to be a cat, can have. How complete and perfect is their enjoyment of existence! Ah! little rogues! your play has been too noisy; you have awakened your mammas; and two or three of the old ewes are getting up; and one of them marching gravely to the troop of lambs has selected her own, given her a gentle butt, and trotted off; the poor re-

buked lamb following meekly, but every now and then stopping
and casting a longing look at its playmates; who, after a
moment's awed pause, had resumed their gambols; whilst the
stately dam every now and then looked back in her turn, to see
that her little one was following. At last she lay down, and the
lamb by her side. I never saw so pretty a pastoral scene in
my life.[1]

Another turning of the dell gives a glimpse of the dark coppice
by which it is backed, and from which we are separated by some
marshy, rushy ground, where the springs have formed into a
pool, and where the moor-hen loves to build her nest. Ay,
there is one scudding away now—I can hear her plash into the
water, and the rustling of her wings amongst the rushes. This
is the deepest part of the wild dingle. How uneven the ground
is! Surely these excavations, now so thoroughly clothed with
vegetation, must originally have been huge gravel pits; there is
no other way of accounting for the labyrinth, for they do dig
gravel in such capricious meanders; but the quantity seems
incredible. Well! there is no end of guessing! We are getting
amongst the springs, and must turn back. Round this corner,
where on ledges like fairy terraces the orchises and arums grow,
and we emerge suddenly on a new side of the dell, just fronting
the small homestead of our good neighbour farmer Allen.

This rustic dwelling belongs to what used to be called in this
part of the country " a little bargain ": thirty or forty acres,

---

[1] I have seen one which affected me much more. Walking in the Church-lane
with one of the young ladies of the vicarage, we met a large flock of sheep, with the
usual retinue of shepherds and dogs. Lingering after them and almost out of sight,
we encountered a straggling ewe, now trotting along, now walking, and every now
and then stopping to look back, and bleating. A little behind her came a lame
lamb, bleating occasionally, as if in answer to its dam, and doing its very best to
keep up with her. It was a lameness of both the fore feet; the knees were bent, and
it seemed to walk on the very edge of the hoof—on tiptoe, if I may venture such an
expression. My young friend thought that the lameness proceeded from original
malformation, I am rather of opinion that it was accidental, and that the poor
creature was wretchedly foot-sore. However that might be, the pain and difficulty
with which it took every step were not to be mistaken; and the distress and fond-
ness of the mother, her perplexity as the flock passed gradually out of sight, the
effort with which the poor lamb contrived to keep up a sort of trot, and their
mutual calls and lamentations were really so affecting, that Ellen and I, although
not at all larmoyante sort of people, had much ado not to cry. We could not find
a boy to carry the lamb, which was too big for us to manage; but I was quite
sure that the ewe would not desert it, and as the dark was coming on, we both
trusted that the shepherds on folding their flock would miss them and return for
them; and so I am happy to say it proved.

perhaps, of arable land, which the owner and his sons cultivated themselves, whilst the wife and daughters assisted in the husbandry, and eked out the slender earnings by the produce of the diary, the poultry yard, and the orchard—an order of cultivators now passing rapidly away, but in which much of the best part of the English character, its industry, its frugality, its sound sense, and its kindness might be found. Farmer Allen himself is an excellent specimen, the cheerful, venerable old man with his long white hair, and his bright grey eye, and his wife is a still finer. They have had a hard struggle to win through the world and keep their little property undivided; but good management and good principles, and the assistance afforded them by an admirable son, who left our village a poor 'prentice boy, and is now a partner in a great house in London, have enabled them to overcome all the difficulties of these trying times, and they are now enjoying the peaceful evening of a well-spent life as free from care and anxiety as their best friends could desire.

Ah! there is Mr Allen in the orchard, the beautiful orchard, with its glorious garlands of pink and white, its pearly pear-blossoms and coral apple-buds. What a flush of bloom it is! How brightly delicate it appears, thrown into strong relief by the dark house and the weather-stained barn, in this soft evening light! The very grass is strewed with the snowy petals of the pear and the cherry. And there sits Mrs Allen, feeding her poultry, with her three little grand-daughters from London, pretty fairies from three years old to five (only two and twenty months elapsed between the birth of the eldest and the youngest) playing round her feet.

Mrs Allen, my dear Mrs Allen, has been that rare thing a beauty, and although she be now an old woman I had almost said that she is so still. Why should I not say so? Nobleness of feature and sweetness of expression are surely as delightful in age as in youth. Her face and figure are much like those which are stamped indelibly on the memory of every one who ever saw that grand specimen of woman—Mrs Siddons. The outline of Mrs Allen's face is exactly the same; but there is more softness, more gentleness, a more feminine composure in the eye and in the smile. Mrs Allen never played Lady Macbeth. Her hair, almost as black as at twenty, is parted on her large fair forehead, and combed under her exquisitely neat and snowy cap; a muslin neck-kerchief, a grey stuff gown, and a white apron complete the picture.

There she sits under an old elder-tree which flings its branches over her like a canopy, whilst the setting sun illumines her venerable figure and touches the leaves with an emerald light; there she sits, placid and smiling, with her spectacles in her hand and a measure of barley on her lap, into which the little girls are dipping their chubby hands and scattering the corn amongst the ducks and chickens with unspeakable glee. But those ingrates the poultry don't seem so pleased and thankful as they ought to be; they mistrust their young feeders. All domestic animals dislike children, partly from an instinctive fear of their tricks and their thoughtlessness; partly, I suspect, from jealousy. Jealousy seems a strange tragic passion to attribute to the inmates of the *basse cour*—but only look at that strutting fellow of a bantam cock (evidently a favourite) who sidles up to his old mistress with an air half affronted and half tender, turning so scornfully from the barleycorns which Annie is flinging towards him, and say if he be not as jealous as Othello! Nothing can pacify him but Mrs Allen's notice and a dole from her hand. See, she is calling to him and feeding him, and now how he swells out his feathers, and flutters his wings, and erects his glossy neck, and struts and crows and pecks, proudest and happiest of bantams, the pet and glory of the poultry yard!

In the meantime my own pet May, who has all this while been peeping into every hole, and penetrating every nook and winding of the dell, in hopes to find another rabbit, has returned to my side, and is sliding her snake-like head into my hand, at once to invite the caress which she likes so well, and to intimate, with all due respect, that it is time to go home. The setting sun gives the same warning; and in a moment we are through the dell, the field, and the gate, past the farm and the mill, and hanging over the bridge that crosses the Loddon river.

What a sunset! how golden! how beautiful! The sun just disappearing, and the narrow liny clouds, which a few minutes ago lay like soft vapoury streaks along the horizon, lighted up with a golden splendour that the eye can scarcely endure, and those still softer clouds which floated above them wreathing and curling into a thousand fantastic forms, as thin and changeful as summer smoke, now defined and deepened into grandeur, and edged with ineffable, insufferable light! Another minute and the brilliant orb totally disappears, and the sky above grows every moment more varied and more beautiful as the dazzling golden lines are mixed with glowing red and gorgeous purple, dappled with small dark specks, and mingled with such a blue as the egg of the hedge-sparrow. To look up at that glorious sky, and then to see that magnificent picture reflected in the clear and lovely Loddon water, is a pleasure never to be described and never forgotten. My heart swells and my eyes fill as I write of it, and think of the immeasurable majesty of nature, and the unspeakable goodness of God, who has spread an enjoyment so pure, so peaceful, and so intense before the meanest and the lowliest of His creatures.

SEPT. 9TH.—A bright sunshiny afternoon. What a comfort it is to get out again—to see once more that rarity of rarities, a fine day! We English people are accused of talking overmuch of the weather; but the weather, this summer, has forced people to talk of it. Summer! did I say? Oh! season most unworthy of that sweet, sunny name! Season of coldness and cloudiness, of gloom and rain! A worse November!—for in November the days are short; and shut up in a warm room, lighted by that household sun, a lamp, one feels through the long evenings comfortably independent of the out-of-door tempests. But though we may have, and did have, fires all through the dog-days, there is no shutting out daylight; and sixteen hours of rain, pattering against the windows and dripping from the eaves—sixteen hours of rain, not merely audible, but visible, for seven days in the week—would be enough to exhaust the patience of Job or Grizzel; especially if Job were a farmer, and Grizzel a country gentlewoman. Never was known such a season! Hay swimming, cattle drowning, fruit rotting, corn spoiling! and that naughty river, the Loddon, who never can take Puff's advice, and "keep between its banks," running about the country, fields, roads, gardens, and houses, like mad! The weather would be talked of. Indeed, it was not easy to talk of anything else. A friend of mine having occasion to write me a letter, thought it worth abusing in rhyme, and bepommelled it through three pages of Bath-guide verse; of which I subjoin a specimen:

> Aquarius surely *reigns* over the world,
> And of late he his water-pot strangely has twirl'd;
> Or he's taken a cullender up by mistake,
> And unceasingly dips it in some mighty lake;
> Though it is not in Lethe—for who can forget
> The annoyance of getting most thoroughly wet?
> It must be in the river called Styx, I declare,
> For the moment it drizzles it makes the men swear.
> ' It did rain to-morrow,' is growing good grammar;
> Vauxhall and camp-stools have been brought to the hammer;
> A pony-gondola is all I can keep,
> And I use my umbrella and pattens in sleep:

Row out of my window, whene'er 'tis my whim
To visit a friend, and just ask, ' Can you swim ? '

So far my friend.[1] In short, whether in prose or in verse, everybody railed at the weather. But this is over now. The sun
has come to dry the world; mud is turned into dust; rivers
have retreated to their proper limits; farmers have left off
grumbling; and we are about to take a walk, as usual, as far
as the Shaw, a pretty wood about a mile off. But one of our
companions being a stranger to the gentle reader, we must do
him the honour of an introduction.

Dogs, when they are sure of having their own way, have
sometimes ways as odd as those of the unfurred, unfeathered
animals, who walk on two legs, and talk, and are called rational.
My beautiful white greyhound, Mayflower,[2] for instance, is as
whimsical as the finest lady in the land. Amongst her other
fancies, she has taken a violent affection for a most hideous
stray dog, who made his appearance here about six months ago,
and contrived to pick up a living in the village, one can hardly
tell how. Now appealing to the charity of old Rachael Strong,
the laundress—a dog-lover by profession; now winning a meal
from the light-footed and open-hearted lasses at the Rose; now
standing on his hind legs, to extort by sheer beggary a scanty
morsel from some pair of " drouthy cronies," or solitary drover,
discussing his dinner or supper on the alehouse bench; now
catching a mouthful, flung to him in pure contempt by some
scornful gentleman of the shoulder-knot, mounted on his throne,
the coach-box, whose notice he had attracted by dint of ugliness;
now sharing the commons of Master Keep the shoemaker's

[1] This friend of mine is a person of great quickness and talent, who, if she were
not a beauty and a woman of fortune—that is to say, if she were prompted by either
of those two powerful *stimuli*, want of money or want of admiration, to take due
pains—would inevitably become a clever writer. As it is, her notes and *jeux d'esprit*,
struck off *à trait de plume*, have great point and neatness. Take the following billet,
which formed the label to a closed basket, containing the ponderous presen
alluded to, last Michaelmas day:

" *To Miss M.*
' When this you see
Remember me,'
Was long a phrase in use;
And so I send
To you, dear friend,
My proxy. ' What ?—A goose! ' "

[2] Dead, alas, since this was written.

pigs; now succeeding to the reversion of the well-gnawed bone of Master Brown the shopkeeper's fierce house-dog; now filching the skim-milk of Dame Wheeler's cat—spit at by the cat; worried by the mastiff; chased by the pigs; screamed at by the dame; stormed at by the shoemaker; flogged by the shopkeeper; teased by all the children, and scouted by all the animals of the parish—but yet living through his griefs, and bearing them patiently, " for sufferance is the badge of all his tribe "—and even seeming to find, in an occasional full meal, or a gleam of sunshine, or a wisp of dry straw on which to repose his sorry carcase, some comfort in his disconsolate condition.

In this plight was he found by May, the most high-blooded and aristocratic of greyhounds; and from this plight did May rescue him; invited him into her territory, the stable; resisted all attempts to turn him out; reinstated him there, in spite of maid and boy, and mistress and master; wore out everybody's opposition, by the activity of her protection, and the pertinacity of her self-will; made him sharer of her bed and of her mess; and, finally, established him as one of the family as firmly as herself.

Dash—for he has even won himself a name amongst us, before he was anonymous—Dash is a sort of a kind of a spaniel; at least there is in his mongrel composition some sign of that beautiful race. Besides his ugliness, which is of the worst sort—that is to say, the shabbiest—he has a limp on one leg that gives a peculiarly one-sided awkwardness to his gait; but independently of his great merit in being May's pet, he has other merits which serve to account for that phenomenon—being, beyond all comparison, the most faithful, attached, and affectionate animal that I have ever known; and that is saying much. He seems to think it necessary to atone for his ugliness by extra good conduct, and does so dance on his lame leg, and so wag his scrubby tail, that it does any one who has a taste for happiness good to look at him—so that he may now be said to stand on his own footing. We are all rather ashamed of him when strangers come in the way, and think it necessary to explain that he is May's pet; but amongst ourselves, and those who are used to his appearance, he has reached the point of favouritism in his own person. I have, in common with wiser women, the feminine weakness of loving whatever loves me—and, therefore, I like Dash. His master has found out that he is a capital finder, and in spite of his lameness will hunt a field or beat a cover with any spaniel in England—and, therefore, *he* likes Dash. The boy has fought a battle, in defence of his beauty, with another boy, bigger than himself, and beat his opponent most handsomely—and, therefore, *he* likes Dash; and the maids like him, or pretend to like him, because we do—as is the fashion of that pliant and imitative class. And now Dash and May follow us everywhere, and are going with us to the Shaw, as I said before—or rather to the cottage by the Shaw, to bespeak milk and butter of our little dairy-woman, Hannah Bint—a housewifely occupation, to which we owe some of our pleasantest rambles.

And now we pass the sunny, dusty village street—who would have thought, a month ago, that we should complain of sun and dust again!—and turn the corner where the two great oaks hang so beautifully over the clear deep pond, mixing their cool green shadows with the bright blue sky, and the white clouds that flit over it; and loiter at the wheeler's shop, always picturesque, with its tools, and its work, and its materials, all so various in form, and so harmonious in colour; and its noisy, merry workmen, hammering and singing, and making a various harmony also. The shop is rather empty to-day, for its usual inmates are busy on the green beyond the pond—one set building a cart, another painting a waggon. And then we leave the village quite behind, and proceed slowly up the cool, quiet lane, between tall hedgerows of the darkest verdure, overshadowing banks green and fresh as an emerald.

Not so quick as I expected, though—for they are shooting here to-day, as Dash and I have both discovered: he with great delight, for a gun to him is as a trumpet to a war-horse; I with no less annoyance, for I don't think that a partridge itself, barring the accident of being killed, can be more startled than I at that abominable explosion. Dash has certainly better blood in his veins than any one would guess to look at him. He even shows some inclination to elope into the fields, in pursuit of those noisy iniquities. But he is an orderly person after all, and a word has checked him.

Ah! here is a shriller din mingling with the small artillery—a shriller and more continuous. We are not yet arrived within sight of Master Weston's cottage, snugly hidden behind a clump of elms; but we are in full hearing of Dame Weston's tongue, raised as usual to scolding pitch. The Westons are new arrivals in our neighbourhood, and the first thing heard of them was a complaint from the wife to our magistrate of her husband's beating her: it was a regular charge of assault—an information in full form. A most piteous case did Dame Weston make of it, softening her voice for the nonce into a shrill tremulous whine, and exciting the mingled pity and anger—pity towards herself, anger towards her husband—of the whole female world, pitiful and indignant as the female world is wont to be on such occasions. Every woman in the parish railed at Master Weston; and poor Master Weston was summoned to attend the bench on the ensuing Saturday, and answer the charge; and such was the clamour abroad and at home, that the unlucky culprit, terrified at the sound of a warrant and a constable, ran away, and was not heard of for a fortnight.

At the end of that time he was discovered, and brought to the bench; and Dame Weston again told her story, and, as before, on the full cry. She had no witnesses, and the bruises of which she made complaint had disappeared, and there were no women present to make common cause with the sex. Still, however, the general feeling was against Master Weston; and it would have gone hard with him when he was called in, if a most unexpected witness had not risen up in his favour. His wife had brought in her arms a little girl about eighteen months old, partly perhaps to move compassion in her favour; for a woman with a child in her arms is always an object that excites kind feelings. The little girl had looked shy and frightened, and had been as quiet as a lamb during her mother's examination; but she no sooner saw her father, from whom she had been a fortnight separated, than she clapped her hands, and laughed, and cried, "Daddy! daddy!" and sprang into his arms, and hung round his neck, and covered him with kisses—again shouting, "Daddy, come home! daddy! daddy!"—and finally nestled her little head in his bosom, with a fulness of contentment, an assurance of tenderness and protection such as no wife-beating tyrant ever did inspire, or ever could inspire, since the days of King Solomon. Our magistrates acted in the very spirit of the Jewish monarch: they accepted the evidence of nature, and dismissed the complaint. And subsequent events have fully justified their decision; Mistress Weston proving not only renowned for the feminine accomplishment of scolding (tongue-banging, it is called in our parts, a compound word which deserves to be Greek), but is actually herself addicted to administering the conjugal discipline, the infliction of which she was pleased to impute to her luckless husband.

Now we cross the stile, and walk up the fields to the Shaw. How beautifully green this pasture looks! and how finely the evening sun glances between the boles of that clump of trees, beech, and ash, and aspen! and how sweet the hedgerows are with woodbine and wild scabious, or, as the country people call it, the gipsy-rose! Here is little Dolly Weston, the unconscious witness, with cheeks as red as a real rose, tottering up the path to meet her father. And here is the carroty-polled urchin, George Coper, returning from work, and singing " Home! sweet Home! " at the top of his voice; and then, when the notes prove too high for him, continuing the air in a whistle, until he has turned the impassable corner; then taking up again the song and the words, " Home! sweet Home! " and looking as if he felt their full import, ploughboy though he be. And so he does; for he is one of a large, an honest, a kind, and an industrious family, where all goes well, and where the poor ploughboy is sure of finding cheerful faces and coarse comforts—all that he has learned to desire. Oh, to be as cheaply and as thoroughly contented as George Coper! All his luxuries, a cricket match!—all his wants satisfied in " home! sweet home! "

Nothing but noises to-day! They are clearing Farmer Brooke's great bean-field, and crying the " Harvest Home! " in a chorus, before which all other sounds—the song, the scolding, the gunnery—fade away, and become faint echoes. A pleasant noise is that! though, for one's ears' sake, one makes some haste to get away from it. And here, in happy time, is that pretty wood, the Shaw, with its broad path-way, its tangled dingles, its nuts and its honeysuckles;—and, carrying away a faggot of those sweetest flowers, we reach Hannah Bint's: of whom, and of whose doings, we shall say more another time.

NOTE.—Poor Dash is also dead. We did not keep him long, indeed I believe that he died of the transition from starvation to good feed, as dangerous to a dog's stomach and to most stomachs, as the less agreeable change from good feed to starvation. He has been succeeded in place and favour by another Dash, not less amiable in demeanour and far more creditable in appearance, bearing no small resemblance to the pet spaniel of my friend Master Dinely, he who stole the bone from the magpies, and who figures as the first Dash of this volume.[1] Let not the unwary reader opine, that in assigning the same name to three several individuals, I am acting as an humble imitator of the inimitable writer who has given immortality to the Peppers and the Mustards, on the one hand; or showing a poverty of invention or a want of acquaintance with the bead-roll of canine appellations on the other. I merely, with my usual scrupulous fidelity, take the names as I find them. The fact is that half the handsome spaniels in England are called Dash, just as half the tall footmen are called Thomas. The name belongs to the species. Sitting in an open carriage one day last summer at the door of a farm-house where my father had some business, I saw a noble and beautiful animal of this kind lying in great state and laziness on the steps, and felt an immediate desire to make acquaintance with him. My father, who had had the same fancy, had patted him and called him " poor fellow " in passing, without eliciting the smallest notice in return. " Dash! " cried I at a venture, " good Dash! noble Dash! " and up he started in a moment, making but one spring from the door into the gig. Of course I was right in my guess. The gentleman's name was Dash.

[1] A reference to an essay in the earliest editions, but not related to " Our Village."—EDITOR.

THE Shaw, leading to Hannah Bint's habitation, is, as I perhaps have said before, a very pretty mixture of wood and coppice; that is to say, a tract of thirty or forty acres covered with fine growing timber—ash, and oak, and elm—very regularly planted; and interspersed here and there with large patches of underwood, hazel, maple, birch, holly, and hawthorn, woven into almost impenetrable thickets by long wreaths of the bramble, the briony, and the brier-rose, or by the pliant and twisting garlands of the wild honeysuckle. In other parts, the Shaw is quite clear of its bosky undergrowth, and clothed only with large beds of feathery fern, or carpets of flowers, primroses, orchises, cowslips, ground-ivy, crane's bill, cotton-grass, Solomon's seal, and forget-me-not, crowded together with a profusion and brilliancy of colour such as I have rarely seen equalled even in a garden. Here the wild hyacinth really enamels the ground with its fresh and lovely purple; there,

> On aged roots, with bright green mosses clad,
> Dwells the wood-sorrel, with its bright thin leaves
> Heart-shaped and triply folded, and its root
> Creeping like beaded coral ; whilst around
> Flourish the copse's pride, anemones,
> With rays like golden studs on ivory laid
> Most delicate ; but touch'd with purple clouds,
> Fit crown for April's fair but changeful brow.

The variety is much greater than I have enumerated; for the ground is so unequal, now swelling in gentle ascents, now dimpling into dells and hollows, and the soil so different in different parts, that the sylvan Flora is unusually extensive and complete.

The season is, however, now too late for this floweriness; and except the tufted woodbines, which have continued in bloom during the whole of this lovely autumn, and some lingering garlands of the purple wild veitch, wreathing round the thickets, and uniting with the ruddy leaves of the bramble, and the pale festoons of the briony, there is little to call one's attention from the grander beauties of the trees—the sycamore, its broad leaves already spotted—the oak, heavy with acorns—and the delicate shining rind of the weeping birch, " the lady of the woods," thrown out in strong relief from a background of holly and hawthorn, each studded with coral berries, and backed with old beeches, beginning to assume the rich tawny hue which makes them perhaps the most picturesque of autumnal trees, as the transparent freshness of their young foliage is undoubtedly the choicest ornament of the forest in spring.

A sudden turn round one of these magnificent beeches brings us to the boundary of the Shaw, and leaning upon a rude gate, we look over an open space of about ten acres of ground, still more varied and broken than that which we have passed, and surrounded on all sides by thick woodland. As a piece of colour, nothing can be well finer. The ruddy glow of the heath-flower, contrasting, on the one hand, with the golden-blossomed furze—on the other, with a patch of buckwheat, of which the bloom is not past, although the grain be ripening, the beautiful buck-wheat, whose transparent leaves and stalks are so brightly tinged with vermilion, while the delicate pink-white of the flower, a paler persicaria, has a feathery fall, at once so rich and so graceful, and a fresh and reviving odour, like that of birch-trees in the dew of a May evening. The bank that surmounts this attempt at cultivation is crowned with the late foxglove and the stately mullein; the pasture of which so great a part of the waste consists, looks as green as an emerald; a clear pond, with the bright sky reflected in it, lets light into the picture; the white cottage of the keeper peeps from the opposite coppice; and the vine-covered dwelling of Hannah Bint rises from amidst the pretty garden, which lies bathed in the sunshine around it.

The living and moving accessories are all in keeping with the cheerfulness and repose of the landscape. Hannah's cow grazing quietly beside the keeper's pony; a brace of fat pointer puppies holding amicable intercourse with a litter of young pigs; ducks, geese, cocks, hens, and chickens scattered over the turf; Hannah herself sallying forth from the cottage door, with her milk-bucket in her hand, and her little brother following with the milking-stool.

My friend, Hannah Bint, is by no means an ordinary person. Her father, Jack Bint (for in all his life he never arrived at the dignity of being called John, indeed in our parts he was commonly known by the cognomen of London Jack), was a drover of high repute in his profession. No man, between Salisbury

Plain and Smithfield, was thought to conduct a flock of sheep so skilfully through all the difficulties of lanes and commons, streets and highroads, as Jack Bint, aided by Jack Bint's famous dog, Watch; for Watch's rough, honest face, black, with a little white about the muzzle, and one white ear, was as well known at fairs and markets, as his master's equally honest and weather-beaten visage. Lucky was the dealer that could secure their services; Watch being renowned for keeping a flock together better than any shepherd's dog on the road—Jack, for delivering them more punctually, and in better condition. No man had a more thorough knowledge of the proper night stations, where good feed might be procured for his charge, and good liquor for Watch and himself; Watch, like other sheep-dogs, being accustomed to live chiefly on bread and beer. His master, though not averse to a pot of good double X, preferred gin; and they who plod slowly along, through wet and weary ways, in frost and in fog, have undoubtedly a stronger temptation to indulge in that cordial and reviving stimulus, than we water-drinkers, sitting in warm and comfortable rooms, can readily imagine. For certain, our drover could never resist the gentle seduction of the gin-bottle, and being of a free, merry, jovial temperament, one of those persons commonly called good fellows, who like to see others happy in the same way with themselves, he was apt to circulate it at his own expense, to the great improvement of his popularity, and the great detriment of his finances.

All this did vastly well whilst his earnings continued proportionate to his spendings, and the little family at home were comfortably supported by his industry: but when a rheumatic fever came on, one hard winter, and finally settled in his limbs, reducing the most active and hardy man in the parish to the state of a confirmed cripple, then his reckless improvidence stared him in the face; and poor Jack, a thoughtless but kind creature, and a most affectionate father, looked at his three motherless children with the acute misery of a parent who has brought those whom he loves best in the world to abject destitution. He found help, where he probably least expected it, in the sense and spirit of his young daughter, a girl of twelve years old.

Hannah was the eldest of the family, and had, ever since her mother's death, which event had occurred two or three years before, been accustomed to take the direction of their domestic concerns, to manage her two brothers, to feed the pigs and the poultry, and to keep house during the almost constant absence of her father. She was a quick, clever lass, of a high spirit, a firm temper, some pride, and a horror of accepting parochial relief, which is every day becoming rarer amongst the peasantry; but which forms the surest safeguard to the sturdy independence of the English character. Our little damsel possessed this quality in perfection; and when her father talked of giving up their comfortable cottage, and removing to the workhouse, whilst she and her brothers must go to service, Hannah formed a bold resolution, and, without disturbing the sick man by any participation of her hopes and fears, proceeded after settling their trifling affairs to act at once on her own plans and designs.

Careless of the future as the poor drover had seemed, he had yet kept clear of debt, and by subscribing constantly to a benefit club, had secured a pittance that might at least assist in supporting him during the long years of sickness and helplessness to which he was doomed to look forward. This his daughter knew. She knew also, that the employer in whose service his health had suffered so severely was a rich and liberal cattle-dealer in the neighbourhood, who would willingly aid an old and faithful servant, and had, indeed, come forward with offers of money. To assistance from such a quarter Hannah saw no objection. Farmer Oakley and the parish were quite distinct things. Of him, accordingly, she asked, not money, but something much more in his own way—" a cow! any cow! old or lame, or what not, so that it were a cow! she would be bound to keep it well; if she did not, he might take it back again. She even hoped to pay for it by and by, by instalments, but that she would not promise! " and partly amused, partly interested by the child's earnestness, the wealthy yeoman gave her, not as a purchase, but as a present, a very fine young Alderney. She then went to the lord of the manor, and, with equal knowledge of character, begged his permission to keep her cow on the Shaw common. " Farmer Oakley had given her a fine Alderney, and she would be bound to pay the rent, and keep her father off the parish, if he would only let it graze on the waste "; and he, too, half from real good nature—half, not to be outdone in liberality by his tenant, not only granted the requested permission, but reduced the rent so much, that the produce of the vine seldom fails to satisfy their kind landlord.

Now, Hannah showed great judgment in setting up as a dairy-woman. She could not have chosen an occupation more completely unoccupied, or more loudly called for. One of the most provoking of the petty difficulties which beset people with a small establishment in this neighbourhood, is the trouble, almost the impossibility, of procuring the pastoral luxuries of milk, eggs, and butter, which rank, unfortunately, amongst the indispensable necessaries of housekeeping. To your thoroughbred Londoner, who, whilst grumbling over his own breakfast, is apt to fancy that thick cream, and fresh butter, and new-laid eggs, grow, so to say, in the country—form an actual part of its natural produce—it may be some comfort to learn, that in this great grazing district, however the calves and the farmers may be the better for cows, nobody else is; that farmers' wives have ceased to keep poultry; and that we unlucky villagers sit down often to our first meal in a state of destitution, which may well make him content with his thin milk and his Cambridge butter, when compared to our imputed pastoralities.

Hannah's Alderney restored us to one rural privilege. Never was so cleanly a little milkmaid. She changed away some of the cottage finery, which, in his prosperous days, poor Jack had pleased himself with bringing home, the China tea-service, the gilded mugs, and the painted waiters, for the useful utensils of the dairy, and speedily established a regular and gainful trade in milk, eggs, butter, honey, and poultry—for poultry they had always kept.

Her domestic management prospered equally. Her father, who retained the perfect use of his hands, began a manufacture of mats and baskets, which he constructed with great nicety and adroitness; the eldest boy, a sharp and clever lad, cut for him his rushes and osiers; erected, under his sister's direction, a shed for the cow, and enlarged and cultivated the garden (always with the good leave of her kind patron the lord of the manor) until it became so ample, that the produce not only kept the pig, and half kept the family, but afforded another branch of merchandise to the indefatigable directress of the establishment. For the younger boy, less quick and active, Hannah contrived to obtain an admission to the charity school, where he made great progress—retaining him at home, however, in the hay-making, and leasing season, or whenever his services could be made available, to the great annoyance of the schoolmaster, whose favourite he is, and who piques himself so much on George's scholarship (your heavy sluggish boy at country work often turns out quick at his book) that it is the general opinion that this much-vaunted pupil will, in process of time, be promoted to the post of assistant, and may, possibly, in course of years, rise to the dignity of a parish pedagogue in his own person; so that his sister, although still making him useful at odd times, now considers George as pretty well off her hands, whilst his elder brother, Tom, could take an under-gardener's place directly, if he were not too important at home to be spared even for a day.

In short, during the five years that she has ruled at the Shaw cottage, the world has gone well with Hannah Bint. Her cow, her calves, her pigs, her bees, her poultry, have each, in their several ways, thriven and prospered. She has even brought Watch to like buttermilk, as well as strong beer, and has nearly persuaded her father (to whose wants and wishes she is most anxiously attentive) to accept of milk as a substitute for gin. Not but Hannah hath had her enemies as well as her betters. Why should she not? The old woman at the lodge, who always piqued herself on being spiteful, and crying down new ways, foretold from the first she would come to no good, and could not forgive her for falsifying her prediction; and Betty Barnes, the slatternly widow of a tippling farmer, who rented a field, and set up a cow herself, and was universally discarded for insufferable dirt, said all that the wit of an envious woman could devise against Hannah and her Alderney; nay, even Ned Miles, the keeper, her next neighbour, who had whilom held entire sway over the Shaw common, as well as its coppices, grumbled as much as so good-natured and genial a person could grumble, when he found a little girl sharing his dominion, a cow grazing beside his pony, and vulgar cocks and hens hovering around the buckwheat destined to feed his noble pheasants. Nobody that had been accustomed to see that paragon of keepers, so tall and manly, and pleasant-looking, with his merry eye, and his knowing smile, striding gaily along, in his green coat, and his gold-laced hat, with Neptune, his noble Newfoundland dog (a retriever is the sporting word), and his beautiful spaniel Flirt at his heels, could conceive how askew he looked, when he first found Hannah and Watch holding equal reign over his old territory, the Shaw common.

Yes! Hannah hath had her enemies; but they are passing away. The old woman at the lodge is dead, poor creature; and Betty Barnes, having herself taken to tippling, has lost the few friends she once possessed, and looks, luckless wretch, as if she would soon die too!—and the keeper?—why, he is not dead, or like to die; but the change that has taken place there is the most

astonishing of all—except, perhaps, the change in Hannah herself.

Few damsels of twelve years old, generally a very pretty age, were less pretty than Hannah Bint. Short and stunted in her figure, thin in face, sharp in feature, with a muddled complexion, wild sun-burnt hair, and eyes whose very brightness had in them something startling, over-informed, super-subtle, too clever for her age—at twelve years old she had quite the air of a little old fairy. Now, at seventeen, matters are mended. Her complexion has cleared; her countenance has developed itself; her figure has shot up into height and lightness, and a sort of rustic grace; her bright, acute eye is softened and sweetened by the womanly wish to please; her hair is trimmed, and curled and brushed, with exquisite neatness; and her whole dress arranged with that nice attention to the becoming, the suitable both in form and texture, which would be called the highest degree of coquetry, if it did not deserve the better name of propriety. Never was such a transmogrification beheld. The lass is really pretty, and Ned Miles has discovered that she is so. There he stands, the rogue, close at her side (for he hath joined her whilst we have been telling her little story, and the milking is over!)—there he stands—holding her milk-pail in one hand, and stroking Watch with the other; whilst she is returning the compliment by patting Neptune's magnificent head. There they stand, as much like lovers as may be; he smiling, and she blushing—he never looking so handsome nor she so pretty in all their lives. There they stand, in blessed forgetfulness of all except each other; as happy a couple as ever trod the earth. There they stand, and one would not disturb them for all the milk and butter in Christendom. I should not wonder if they were fixing the wedding day.

NOV. 6TH.—The weather is as peaceful to-day, as calm, and as mild, as in early April; and, perhaps, an autumn afternoon and a spring morning do resemble each other more in feeling, and even in appearance, than any two periods of the year. There is in both the same freshness and dewiness of the herbage; the same balmy softness in the air; and the same pure and lovely blue sky, with white fleecy clouds floating across it. The chief difference lies in the absence of flowers, and the presence of leaves. But then the foliage of November is so rich, and glowing, and varied, that it may well supply the place of the gay blossoms of the spring; whilst all the flowers of the field or the garden could never make amends for the want of leaves—that beautiful and graceful attire in which nature has clothed the rugged forms of trees—the verdant drapery to which the landscape owes its loveliness, and the forests their glory.

If choice must be between two seasons, each so full of charm, it is at least no bad philosophy to prefer the present good, even whilst looking gratefully back, and hopefully forward, to the past and the future. And of a surety, no fairer specimen of a November day could well be found than this—a day made to wander

> By yellow commons and birch-shaded hollows,
> And hedgerows bordering unfrequented lanes ;

nor could a prettier country be found for our walk than this shady and yet sunny Berkshire, where the scenery, without rising into grandeur or breaking into wildness, is so peaceful, so cheerful, so varied, and so thoroughly English.

We must bend our steps towards the water side, for I have a message to leave at Farmer Riley's: and sooth to say, it is no unpleasant necessity; for the road thither is smooth and dry, retired, as one likes a country walk to be, but not too lonely, which women never like; leading past the Loddon—the bright, brimming, transparent Loddon—a fitting mirror for this bright blue sky, and terminating at one of the prettiest and most comfortable farm-houses in the neighbourhood.

How beautiful the lane is to-day, decorated with a thousand colours! The brown road, and the rich verdure that borders it, strewed with the pale yellow leaves of the elm, just beginning to fall; hedgerows glowing with long wreaths of the bramble in every variety of purplish red; and overhead the unchanged green of the fir, contrasting with the spotted sycamore, the tawny beech, and the dry sere leaves of the oak, which rustle as the light wind passes through them; a few common hardy yellow flowers (for yellow is the common colour of flowers, whether wild or cultivated, as blue is the rare one), flowers of many sorts, but almost of one tint, still blowing in spite of the season, and ruddy berries glowing through all. How very beautiful is the lane!

And how pleasant is this hill where the road widens, with the group of cattle by the wayside, and George Hearn, the little post-boy, trundling his hoop at full speed, making all the better haste in his work, because he cheats himself into thinking it play! And how beautiful, again, is this patch of common at the hill-top with the clear pool, where Martha Pither's children —elves of three, and four, and five years old—without any distinction of sex in their sunburnt faces and tattered drapery, are dipping up water in their little homely cups shining with cleanliness, and a small brown pitcher with the lip broken, to fill that great kettle, which, when it is filled, their united strength will never be able to lift! They are quite a group for a painter, with their rosy cheeks, and chubby hands, and round merry faces; and the low cottage in the background, peeping out of its vine leaves and china roses, with Martha at the door, tidy, and comely, and smiling, preparing the potatoes for the pot, and watching the progress of dipping and filling that useful utensil, completes the picture.

But we must get on. No time for more sketches in these short days. It is getting cold too. We must proceed in our walk. Dash is showing us the way and beating the thick double hedgerow that runs along the side of the meadows, at a rate that indicates games astir, and causes the leaves to fly as fast as an east wind after a hard frost. Ah! a pheasant! a superb cock pheasant! Nothing is more certain than Dash's questing, whether in a hedgerow or covert, for a better spaniel never went into the field; but I fancied that it was a hare afoot, and was almost as much startled to hear the whirring of those splendid wings, as the princely bird himself would have been at the report of a gun. Indeed, I believe, that the way in which a pheasant

H

goes off, does sometimes make young sportsmen a little nervous (they don't own it very readily, but the observation may be relied on nevertheless), until they get as it were broken in to the sound; and then that grand and sudden burst of wing becomes as pleasant to them, as it seems to be to Dash, who is beating the hedgerow with might and main, and giving tongue louder, and sending the leaves about faster than ever—very proud of finding the pheasant, and perhaps a little angry with me for not shooting it; at least looking as if he would be angry if I were a man; for Dash is a dog of great sagacity, and has doubtless not lived four years in the sporting world without making the discovery, that although gentlemen do shoot, ladies do not.

The Loddon at last! the beautiful Loddon! and the bridge, where every one stops, as by instinct, to lean over the rails, and gaze a moment on a landscape of surpassing loveliness—the fine grounds of the Great House, with their magnificent groups of limes, and firs, and poplars grander than ever poplars were; the green meadows opposite, studded with oaks and elms; the clear winding river; the mill with its picturesque old buildings bounding the scene; all glowing with the rich colouring of autumn, and harmonized by the soft beauty of the clear blue sky, and the delicious calmness of the hour. The very peasant whose daily path it is, cannot cross that bridge without a pause.

But the day is wearing fast, and it grows colder and colder. I really think it will be a frost. After all, spring is the pleasantest season, beautiful as this scenery is. We must get on. Down that broad yet shadowy lane, between the park, dark with evergreens and dappled with deer, and the meadows where sheep, and cows, and horses are grazing under the tall elms; that lane where the wild bank, clothed with fern, and tufted with furze, and crowned by rich berried thorn, and thick shining holly on the one side, seems to vie in beauty with the picturesque old paling, the bright laurels, and the plumy cedars, on the other; down that shady lane, until the sudden turn brings us to an opening where four roads meet, where a noble avenue turns down to the Great House; where the village church rears its modest spire from amidst its venerable yew-trees; and where, embosomed in orchards and gardens, and backed by barns and ricks, and all the wealth of the farm-yard, stands the spacious and comfortable abode of good Farmer Riley—the end and object of our walk.

And in happy time the message is said, and the answer given, for this beautiful mild day is edging off into a dense frosty evening; the leaves of the elm and the linden in the old avenue are quivering and vibrating and fluttering in the air, and at length falling crisply on the earth, as if Dash were beating for pheasants in the tree tops; the sun gleams dimly through the

fog, giving little more of light or heat than his fair sister the lady moon—I don't know a more disappointing person than a cold sun; and I am beginning to wrap my cloak closely round me, and to calculate the distance to my own fireside, recanting all the way my praises of November, and longing for the showery, flowery April as much as if I were a half-chilled butterfly, or a dahlia knocked down by the frost.

Ah, dear me! what a climate this is, that one cannot keep in the same mind about it for half an hour together! I wonder by the way whether the fault is in the weather, which Dash does not seem to care for, or in me? If I should happen to be wet through in a shower next spring, and should catch myself longing for autumn, that would settle the question.

I DOUBT if there be any scene in the world more animating or delightful than a cricket match—I do not mean a set match at Lord's Ground for money, hard money, between a certain number of gentlemen and players, as they are called—people who make a trade of that noble sport, and degrade it into an affair of bettings, and hedgings, and cheatings, it may be, like boxing or horse-racing; nor do I mean a pretty fête in a gentleman's park, where one club of cricketing dandies encounter another such club, and where they show off in graceful costume to a gay marquee of admiring belles, who condescend so to purchase admiration, and while away a long summer morning in partaking cold collations, conversing occasionally, and seeming to understand the game—the whole being conducted according to ballroom etiquette, so as to be exceedingly elegant and exceedingly dull. No! the cricket that I mean is a real solid old-fashioned match between neighbouring parishes, where each attacks the other for honour and a supper, glory and half a crown a man. If there be any gentlemen amongst them, it is well—if not, it is so much the better. Your gentleman cricketer is in general rather an anomalous character. Elderly gentlemen are obviously good for nothing; and young beaux are, for the most part, hampered and trammelled by dress and habit; the stiff cravat, the pinched-in waist, the dandy-walk—oh, they will never do for cricket! Now, our country lads, accustomed to the flail or the hammer (your blacksmiths are capital hitters), have the free use of their arms; they know how to move their shoulders; and they can move their feet too—they can run; then they are so much better made, so much more athletic, and yet so much lissomer—to use a Hampshire phrase, which deserves at least to be good English. Here and there, indeed, one meets with an old Etonian, who retains his boyish love for that game which formed so considerable a branch of his education: some even preserve their boyish proficiency, but in general it wears away like the Greek, quite as certainly, and almost as fast: a few years of Oxford, or Cambridge, or the continent, are sufficient to annihilate both the power and the inclination. No! a village match is the thing—where our highest officer—our conductor (to borrow a musical term) is but a little farmer's second son; where a day labourer is our bowler, and a blacksmith our long-stop; where the spectators consist of the retired cricketers, the veterans of the green, the careful mothers, the girls, and all the boys of two parishes, together with a few amateurs, little above them in rank, and not at all in pretension; where laughing and shouting, and the very ecstasy of merriment and good humour, prevail: such a match, in short, as I attended yesterday, at the expense of getting twice wet through, and as I would attend to-morrow, at the certainty of having that ducking doubled.

For the last three weeks our village has been in a state of great excitement, occasioned by a challenge from our north-western neighbours, the men of B., to contend with us at cricket. Now we have not been much in the habit of playing matches. Three or four years ago, indeed, we encountered the men of S., our neighbours south-by-east, with a sort of doubtful success, beating them on our own ground, whilst they in the second match returned the compliment on theirs. This discouraged us. Then an unnatural coalition between a high-church curate and an evangelical gentleman-farmer drove our lads from the Sunday-evening practice, which, as it did not begin before both services were concluded, and as it tended to keep the young men from the ale-house, our magistrates had winked at, if not encouraged. The sport therefore had languished until the present season, when under another change of circumstances the spirit began to revive. Half a dozen fine active lads, of influence amongst their comrades, grew into men and yearned for cricket; an enterprising publican gave a set of ribands: his rival, mine host of the Rose, an out-doer by profession, gave two; and the clergyman and his lay ally, both well-disposed and good-natured men, gratified by the submission to their authority, and finding, perhaps, that no great good resulted from the substitution of public-houses for out-of-door diversions, relaxed. In short the practice recommenced, and the hill was again alive with men and boys, and innocent merriment; but farther than the riband matches amongst ourselves nobody dreamed of going, till this challenge—we were modest, and doubted our own strength. The B. people, on the other hand, must have been braggers born, a whole parish of gasconaders. Never was such boasting!

such crowing! such ostentatious display of practice! such mutual compliments from man to man—bowler to batter, batter to bowler! It was a wonder they did not challenge all England. It must be confessed that we were a little astounded; yet we firmly resolved not to decline the combat; and one of the most spirited of the new growth, William Grey by name, took up the glove in a style of manly courtesy that would have done honour to a knight in the days of chivalry. "We were not professed players," he said; "being little better than school-boys, and scarcely older; but, since they had done us the honour to challenge us, we would try our strength. It would be no discredit to be beaten by such a field."

Having accepted the wager of battle, our champion began forthwith to collect his forces. William Grey is himself one of the finest youths that one shall see—tall, active, slender and yet strong, with a piercing eye full of sagacity, and a smile full of good-humour—a farmer's son by station, and used to hard work as farmers' sons are now, liked by everybody, and admitted to be an excellent cricketer. He immediately set forth to muster his men, remembering with great complacency that Samuel Long, a bowler *comme il y en a peu*, the very man who had knocked down nine wickets, had beaten us, bowled us out at the fatal return match some years ago at S., had luckily, in a remove of a quarter of a mile last Lady-day, crossed the boundaries of his old parish, and actually belonged to us. Here was a stroke of good fortune! Our captain applied to him instantly; and he agreed at a word. Indeed Samuel Long is a very civilized person. He is a middle-aged man, who looks rather old amongst our young lads, and whose thickness and breadth give no token of remarkable activity; but he is very active, and so steady a player! so safe! We had half gained the match when we had secured him. He is a man of substance, too, in every way; owns one cow, two donkeys, six pigs, and geese and ducks beyond count; dresses like a farmer, and owes no man a shilling; and all this from pure industry, sheer day-labour. Note that your good cricketer is commonly the most industrious man in the parish; the habits that make him such are precisely those which make a good workman—steadiness, sobriety, and activity —Samuel Long might pass for the beau ideal of the two characters. Happy were we to possess him! Then we had another piece of good luck. James Brown, a journeyman blacksmith and a native, who, being of a rambling disposition, had roamed from place to place for half a dozen years, had just returned to settle with his brother at another corner of our village, bringing with him a prodigious reputation in cricket and in gallantry— the gay Lothario of the neighbourhood. He is said to have made more conquests in love and in cricket than any blacksmith in the county. To him also went the indefatigable William Grey, and he also consented to play. No end to our good fortune! Another celebrated batter, called Joseph Hearne, had likewise recently married into the parish. He worked, it is true, at the A. mills, but slept at the house of his wife's father in our territories. He also was sought and found by our leader. But he was grand and shy; made an immense favour of the thing; courted courting and then hung back; " Did not know that he could be spared; had partly resolved not to play again—at least not this season; thought it rash to accept the challenge; thought they might do without him——" " Truly I think so too," said our spirited champion; " we will not trouble you, Mr Hearne."

Having thus secured two powerful auxiliaries, and rejected a third, we began to reckon and select the regular native forces. Thus ran our list: William Grey, 1.—Samuel Long, 2.—James Brown, 3.—George and John Simmons, one capital, the other so-so—an uncertain hitter, but a good fieldsman, 5.—Joel Brent, excellent, 6.—Ben Appleton—Here was a little pause—Ben's abilities at cricket were not completely ascertained; but then he was so good a fellow, so full of fun and waggery! no doing without Ben. So he figured in the list, 7.—George Harris—a short halt there too! Slowish—slow but sure. I think the proverb brought him in, 8.—Tom Coper—oh, beyond the world, Tom Coper! the red-headed gardening lad, whose left-handed strokes send *her* (a cricket-ball, like that other moving thing a ship, is always of the feminine gender), send her spinning a mile, 9.—Harry Willis, another blacksmith, 10.

We had now ten of our eleven, but the choice of the last occasioned some demur. Three young Martins, rich farmers of the neighbourhood, successively presented themselves, and were all rejected by our independent and impartial general for want of merit—*cricketal* merit. " Not good enough," was his pithy answer. Then our worthy neighbour, the half-pay lieutenant, offered his services,—he, too, though with some hesitation and modesty, was refused—" Not quite young enough " was his sentence. John Strong, the exceeding long son of our dwarfish mason, was the next candidate—a nice youth—everybody likes John Strong—and a willing, but so tall and so limp, bent in the middle—a thread-paper, six feet high! We were all afraid that, in spite of his name, his strength would never hold out. " Wait till next year, John," quoth William Grey, with all the dignified seniority of twenty speaking to eighteen. " Coper's a year younger," said John. " Coper's a foot shorter," replied William: so John retired; and the eleventh man remained unchosen, almost to the eleventh hour. The eve of the match arrived, and the post was still vacant, when a little boy of fifteen, David Willis, brother to Harry, admitted by accident to the last practice, saw eight of them out, and was voted in by acclamation.

That Sunday evening's practice (for Monday was the important day) was a period of great anxiety, and, to say the truth, of great pleasure. There is something strangely delightful in the innocent spirit of party. To be one of a numerous body, to be authorized to say *we*, to have a rightful interest in triumph or defeat, is gratifying at once to social feeling and to personal pride. There was not a ten-year-old urchin, or a septuagenary woman in the parish, who did not feel an additional importance, a reflected consequence, in speaking of " our side." An election interests in the same way; but that feeling is less pure. Money is there, and hatred, and politics, and lies. Oh, to be a voter, or a voter's wife, comes nothing near the genuine and hearty sympathy of belonging to a parish, breathing the same air, looking on the same trees, listening to the same nightingales! Talk of a patriotic elector!—Give me a parochial patriot, a man who loves his parish! Even we, the female partisans, may partake the common ardour. I am sure I did. I never, though tolerably eager and enthusiastic at all times, remember being in a more delicious state of excitation than on the eve of that battle. Our hopes waxed stronger and stronger. Those of our players who were present, were excellent. William Grey got forty notches off his own bat; and that brilliant hitter, Tom Coper, gained eight from two successive balls. As the evening advanced, too, we had encouragement of another sort. A spy, who had been despatched to reconnoitre the enemy's quarters, returned from their practising ground with a most consolatory report. " Really," said Charles Grover, our intelligencer—a

fine old steady judge, one who had played well in his day
—" they are no better than so many old women. Any five
of ours would beat their eleven." This sent us to bed in high
spirits.

Morning dawned less favourably. The sky promised a series
of deluging showers, and kept its word as English skies are wont
to do on such occasions; and a lamentable message arrived at
the headquarters from our trusty comrade Joel Brent. His
master, a great farmer, had begun the hay harvest that very
morning, and Joel, being as eminent in one field as in another,
could not be spared. Imagine Joel's plight! the most ardent of
all our eleven! a knight held back from the tourney! a soldier
from the battle! The poor swain was inconsolable. At last, one
who is always ready to do a good-natured action, great or little,
set forth to back his petition; and, by dint of appealing to the
public spirit of our worthy neighbour and the state of the
barometer, talking alternately of the parish honour and thunder
showers, of lost matches and sopped hay, he carried his point,
and returned triumphantly with the delighted Joel.

In the meantime we became sensible of another defalcation.
On calling over our roll, Brown was missing; and the spy of
the preceding night, Charles Grover—the universal scout and
messenger of the village, a man who will run half a dozen miles
for a pint of beer, who does errands for the very love of the
trade, who, if he had been a lord, would have been an am-
bassador—was instantly despatched to summon the truant. His
report spread general consternation. Brown had set off at four
o'clock in the morning to play in a cricket match at M., a little
town twelve miles off, which had been his last residence. Here
was desertion! Here was treachery! Here was treachery
against that goodly state, our parish! To send James Brown to
Coventry was the immediate resolution; but even that seemed
too light a punishment for such delinquency. Then how we
cried him down! At ten on Sunday night (for the rascal had
actually practised with us, and never said a word of his intended
disloyalty) he was our faithful mate, and the best player (take
him for all in all) of the eleven. At ten in the morning he had
run away, and we were well rid of him; he was no batter compared with William Grey or Tom Coper; not fit to wipe the
shoes of Samuel Long, as a bowler; nothing of a scout to John
Simmons; the boy David Willis was worth fifty of him—

I trust we have within our realm
Five hundred good as he.

was the universal sentiment. So we took tall John Strong, who, with an incurable hankering after the honour of being admitted, had kept constantly with the players, to take the chance of some such accident—we took John for our *pis-aller*. I never saw any one prouder than the good-humoured lad was of this not very flattering piece of preferment.

John Strong was elected, and Brown sent to Coventry; and, when I first heard of his delinquency, I thought the punishment only too mild for the crime. But I have since learned the secret history of the offence (if we could know the secret histories of all offences, how much better the world would seem than it does now!); and really my wrath is much abated. It was a piece of gallantry, of devotion to the sex, or rather a chivalrous obedience to one chosen fair. I must tell my readers the story. Mary Allen, the prettiest girl of M., had it seems revenged upon our blacksmith the numberless inconsistencies of which he stood accused. He was in love over head and ears, but the nymph was cruel. She said no, and no, and no, and poor Brown, three times rejected, at last resolved to leave the place, partly in despair, and partly in that hope which often mingles strangely with a lover's despair, the hope that when he was gone he should be missed. He came home to his brother's accordingly; but for five weeks he heard nothing from or of the inexorable Mary, and was glad to beguile his own " vexing thoughts," by endeavouring to create in his mind an artificial and factitious interest in our cricket match—all unimportant as such a·trifle must have seemed to a man in love. Poor James, however, is a social and warm-hearted person, not likely to resist a contagious sympathy. As the time for the play advanced, the interest which he had at first affected became genuine and sincere: and he was really, when he left the ground on Sunday night, almost as enthusiastically absorbed in the event of the next day as Joel Brent himself. He little foresaw the new and delightful interest which awaited him at home, where, on the moment of his arrival, his sister-in-law and confidante presented him with a billet from the lady of his heart. It had, with the usual delay of letters sent by private hands in that rank of life, loitered on the road, in a degree inconceivable to those who are accustomed to the punctual speed of the post, and had taken ten days for its twelve miles' journey.

Have my readers any wish to see this *billet-doux*? I can show them (but in strict confidence) a literal copy. It was addressed,

" For mistur jem browne
blaxmith by
S."

The inside ran thus: " Mistur browne this is to Inform yew that oure parish plays bramley men next monday is a week, i think we shall lose without yew. from your humbell servant to command

MARY ALLEN "

Was there ever a prettier relenting? a summons more flattering, more delicate, more irresistible? The precious epistle was undated; but, having ascertained who brought it, and found, by cross-examining the messenger, that the Monday in question was the very next day, we were not surprised to find that *Mistur browne* forgot his engagement to us, forgot all but Mary and Mary's letter, and set off at four o'clock the next morning to walk twelve miles, and play for her parish, and in her sight. Really we must not send James Brown to Coventry— must we? Though if, as his sister-in-law tells our damsel Harriet he hopes to do, he should bring the fair Mary home as his bride, he will not greatly care how little we say to him. But he must not be sent to Coventry—True-love forbid!

At last we were all assembled, and marched down to H. common, the appointed ground, which, though in our dominions according to the map, was the constant practising place of our opponents, and *terra incognita* to us. We found our adversaries on the ground as we expected, for our various delays had hindered us from taking the field so early as we wished; and, as soon as we had settled all preliminaries, the match began.

But, alas! I have been so long settling my preliminaries that I have left myself no room for the detail of our victory, and must squeeze the account of our grand achievements into as little compass as Cowley, when he crammed the names of eleven of his mistresses into the narrow space of four eight-syllable lines. *They* began the warfare—these boastful men of B. And what think you, gentle reader, was the amount of their innings? These challengers—the famous eleven—how many did they get? Think! imagine! guess!—You cannot?—Well!—they got twenty-two, or, rather, they got twenty; for two of theirs were short notches, and would never have been allowed, only that, seeing what they were made of, we and our umpires were not particular.—They should have had twenty more, if they had chosen to claim them. Oh, how well we fielded! and how well we bowled! our good play had quite as much to do with their miserable failure as their bad. Samuel Long is a slow bowler, George Simmons a fast one, and the change from Long's lobbing to Simmons's fast balls posed them completely. Poor simpletons! they were always wrong, expecting the slow for the quick, and the quick for the slow. Well, we went in. And what were our innings? Guess again!—guess! A hundred and sixty-nine! in spite of soaking showers, and wretched ground, where the ball would not run a yard, we headed them by a hundred and forty-seven; and then they gave in, as well they might. William Grey pressed them much to try another innings. " There was so much chance," as he courteously observed, " in cricket, that advantageous as our position seemed, we might, very possibly, be overtaken. The B. men had better try." But they were beaten sulky, and would not move—to my great disappointment; I wanted to prolong the pleasure of success. What a glorious sensation it is to be for five hours together winning—winning—winning! always feeling what a whist-player feels when he takes up four honours, seven trumps! Who would think that a little bit of leather, and two pieces of wood, had such a delightful and delighting power?

The only drawback on my enjoyment was the failure of the pretty boy, David Willis, who injudiciously put in first, and playing for the first time in a match amongst men and strangers, who talked to him, and stared at him, was seized with such a fit of shamefaced shyness that he could scarcely hold his bat, and was bowled out without a stroke, from actual nervousness. " He will come off that," Tom Coper says.—I am afraid he will. I wonder whether Tom had ever any modesty to lose. Our other modest lad, John Strong, did very well; his length told in fielding, and he got good fame. Joel Brent, the rescued mower, got into a scrape, and out of it again; his fortune for the day. He ran out his mate, Samuel Long; who, I do believe, but for the excess of Joel's eagerness, would have stayed in till this time, by which exploit he got into sad disgrace; and then he himself got thirty-seven runs, which redeemed his reputation. William Grey made a hit which actually lost the cricket ball. We think she lodged in a hedge, a quarter of a mile off, but nobody could find her. And George Simmons had nearly lost his shoe, which he tossed away in a passion, for having been caught out, owing to the ball glancing against it. These, together with a very complete somerset of Ben Appleton, our long-stop, who floundered about in the mud, making faces and attitudes as laughable as Grimaldi, none could tell whether by accident or design, were the chief incidents of the scene of action. Amongst the spectators nothing remarkable occurred, beyond the general calamity of two or three drenchings, except that a form, placed by the side of a hedge, under a very insufficient shelter, was knocked into the ditch, in a sudden rush of the cricketers to escape a pelting shower, by which means all parties shared the fate of Ben Appleton, some on land and some by water; and that, amidst the scramble, a saucy gipsy of a girl contrived to steal from the knee of the demure and well-apparelled Samuel Long, a smart handkerchief, which his careful dame had tied around it, to preserve his new (what is the mincing feminine word?)—his new—inexpressibles; thus reversing the story of Desdemona, and causing the new Othello to call aloud for his handkerchief, to the great diversion of the company. And so we parted; the players retired to their supper, and we to our homes; all wet through, all good-humoured, and all happy— except the losers.

To-day we are happy too. Hats, with ribands in them, go glancing up and down; and William Grey says, with a proud humility, "We do not challenge any parish; but if we be challenged, we are ready."

THE finest young man in our village is undoubtedly Joel Brent, half-brother to my Lizzy. They are alike too; as much alike as a grown-up person and a little child of different sexes well can be; alike in a vigorous uprightness of form, light, firm, and compact as possible; alike in the bright, sparkling, triumphant blue eye, the short curled upper lip, the brown wavy hair, the white forehead and sunburnt cheeks, and, above all, in the singular spirit and gaiety of their countenance and demeanour, the constant expression of life and glee, to which they owe the best and rarest part of their attractiveness. They seem, and they are, two of the happiest and merriest creatures that ever trod on the green sward. Really to see Joel walking by the side of his team (for this enviable mortal, the pride of our village, is by calling a carter), to see him walking, on a fine sunny morning, by the side of his bell-team, the fore-horse decked with ribbons and flowers like a countess on the birth-day, as consciously handsome as his driver, the long whip poised gracefully on his shoulder, his little sister in his hand, and his dog Ranger (a beautiful red and white spaniel :—everything that belongs to Joel is beautiful) frisking about them—to see this group, and to hear the merry clatter formed by Lizzy's tongue, Joel's whistling, and Ranger's delightful bark, is enough to put an amateur of pleasant sounds and happy faces in good-humour for the day.

It is a grateful sight in other respects, for Joel is a very picturesque person, just such an one as a painter would select for the foreground of some English landscape, where nature is shown in all her loveliness. His costume is the very perfection of rustic coquetry, of that grace, which all admire and few practise, the grace of adaptation, the beauty of fitness. No one ever saw Joel in that wretched piece of deformity a coat, or that still wretcheder apology for a coat a dock-tailed jacket. Broadcloth, the " common stale " of peer and peasant, approaches him not; neither does " the poor creature," fustian. His upper garment consists of that prettier jacket without skirts,—call it for the more grace a doublet,—of dark velveteen, hanging open over his waistcoat, giving a Spanish or an Italian air to his whole appearance, and setting off to great advantage his trim yet manly shape. To this he adds a silk handkerchief, tied very loosely round his neck, a shirt collar open so as to show his throat, as you commonly see in the portraits of artists, very loose trousers, and a straw hat. Sometimes in cold weather he throws over all a smock-frock, and last winter brought up a fashion amongst our lads, by assuming one of that light blue Waterloo, such as butchers wear. As soon as all his comrades had provided themselves with a similar piece of rustic finery, he abandoned his, and indeed generally sticks to his velveteen jacket, which, by some magical influence of cleanliness and neatness, always looks new. I cannot imagine how he contrives it, but dirt never hangs upon Joel; even a fall at cricket in the summer, or a tumble on the ice in the winter, fails to soil him; and he is so ardent in his diversions, and so little disposed to let his coxcombry interfere with his sports, that both have been pretty often tried; the former especially.

Ever since William Grey's secession, which took place shortly after our great match, for no cause assigned, Joel has been the leader and chief of our cricketers. Perhaps, indeed, Joel's rapid improvement might be one cause of William's withdrawal, for, without attributing anything like envy or jealousy to these fine young men, we all know that " two stars keep not their motion in one sphere," and so forth, and if it were absolutely necessary that either our " Harry Hotspur, or the Prince of Wales," should abdicate that fair kingdom the cricket-ground, I must say that I am content to retain our present champion. Joel is in my mind the better player, joining to William's agility and certainty of hand and eye, all the ardour, force, and gaiety of his own quick and lively spirit. The whole man is in the game, mind and body; and his success is such as dexterity and enthusiasm united must always command. To be sure he is a *leetle* over-eager, *that* I must confess, and does occasionally run out a slow mate; but he is sure to make up for it by his own exertions, and after all what a delightful fault zeal is! Now that we are on the subject of faults, it must be said, not that Joel has his share, which is of course, but that they are exceedingly venial, little shades that become him, and arise out of his brighter qualities as smoke from the flame. Thus, if he sometimes steals one of his active holidays for a revel or a cricket match, he is sure to make up the loss to his master by a double portion of labour the next day; and if now and then, at tide-times, he loiters in the chimney-corner at the Rose, rather longer than strict prudence might warrant, no one can hear his laugh and his song pouring through the open door, like the very voice of " jest and youthful jollity," without feeling certain that it is good fellowship, and not good liquor, that detains him. Indeed, so much is he the delight of the country lads, who frequent that well-accustomed inn, so much is his company sought after in all rustic junketings, that I am only astonished at the strength of resolution, and power of resisting temptation, which he displays in going thither so seldom.

If our village lads be so fond of him, it is not to be doubted that our village maidens like him too. The pretty brunette, Sally Wheeler, who left a good service at B., to take in needle-work, and come home to her grandmother, she being, to use Sally's phrase, " unked for want of company " (N.B. Dame Wheeler is as deaf as a post, a cannon would not rouse her), is thought, in our little world, to have had an eye to Joel in this excess of dutifulness. Miss Phœbe, the lass of the Rose, she also, before her late splendid marriage to the patten-maker, is said to have becurled and beflounced herself at least two tiers higher on club-nights, and Sundays, and holidays, and whenever there was a probable chance of meeting him. The gay recruiting sergeant, and all other beaux, were abandoned the instant he appeared; nay, it is even hinted that the patten-maker owes his fair bride partly to pique at Joel's indifference. Then Miss Sophia Matthews, the schoolmistress on the lea, to whom in point of dignity Miss Phœbe was nothing, who wears a muff and a veil, walks mincingly, and tosses her head in the air, keeps a maid—a poor little drab of ten years old; follows, as she says, a genteel profession—I think she may have twenty scholars at eightpence a week; and when she goes to dine with her brother, the collar-maker, hires a boy for a penny to carry her clogs— Miss Sophia, it is well known, hath pretermitted her dignity in the matter of Joel; hath invited the whole family to tea (only think of Joel at a tea-party!), hath spoken of him as " a person above the common; a respectable young man; one, who with a discreet and accomplished wife, a woman of reading and educa-tion " (Miss Sophia, in the days of her father, the late collar-maker of happy memory, before she " taught the young idea how to shoot," had herself drunk deeply at that well of know-

ledge, the circulating library of B.), " not too young " (Miss
Sophia calls herself twenty-eight—I wonder what the register
says!), " No brazen-faced gipsy, like Sally Wheeler " (Miss
Sophia's cast of countenance is altogether different from Sally's
dark and sparkling beauty, she being pink-eyed, red-haired,
lean, pale, and freckled), " or the jill-flirt Phœbe "——but to
cut short an oration which, in spite of the lady's gentility, began
to grow rather scurrilous, one fact was certain—that Joel might,
had he so chosen, have worn the crown matrimonial in Miss
Sophia's territories, consisting of a freehold cottage a little the
worse for wear, a good garden, a capital orchard, and an extensive right of common; to say nothing of the fair damsel and
her school, or, as she is accustomed to call it, her seminary.

Joel's proud bright eye glanced, however, carelessly over all.
There was little perceptible difference of feeling in the gay
distant smile with which he regarded the coquettish advances
of the pretty brunette, Sally Wheeler, or the respectful bow with
which he retreated from the undignified condescension of Miss
Sophia. He fluttered about our village belles like a butterfly over
a bed of tulips; sometimes approaching them for a moment, and
seeming then ready to fix, but oftener above and out of reach,
a creature of a sprightlier element, too buoyant and volatile to
light on an earthly flower. At last, however, the rover was
caught; and our damsel, Harriet, had the glory of winning that
indomitable heart.

Now Harriet is in all things Lucy's successor; in post, and
favour, and beauty, and lovers. In my eye she is still prettier
than Lucy; there is something so feminine and so attractive
in her loveliness. She is a tall young woman, finely, though, for
eighteen, rather fully, formed; with a sweet child-like face, a
fair blooming complexion, a soft innocent smile, and the eye
of a dove. Add to this a gentle voice, a quiet modest manner,
and a natural gentility of appearance, and no wonder that
Harriet might vie with her predecessor in the number of her
admirers. She inherited also a spice of her coquetry, although
it was shown in so different a way that we did not immediately
find it out. Lucy was a flirt active; Harriet was a flirt passive:
Lucy talked to her beaux; Harriet only listened to hers: Lucy,
when challenged on the number of her conquests, denied the
thing, and blushed, and laughed, and liked to be laughed at;
Harriet, on a similar charge, gave no token of liking or denial,

but said quietly that she could not help it, and went on winning hearts by dozens, prodigal of smiles but chary of love, till Joel came, " pleased her by manners most unlike her own," and gave to her delicate womanly beauty the only charms it wanted —sensibility and consciousness.

The manner in which we discovered this new flirtation, which, unlike her others, was concealed with the pretty reserve and mystery that wait on true love, was sufficiently curious. We had noted Joel more frequently than common about the house : sometimes he came for Lizzy ; sometimes to bring news of a cricket match ; sometimes to ask questions about bats and balls ; sometimes to see if his dog Ranger had followed my May ; sometimes to bring me a nosegay. All this occasioned no suspicion ; we were too glad to see Joel to think of inquiring why he came. But when the days shortened, and evening closed in dark and cold before his work was done, and cricket and flowers were over, and May and Lizzy safe in their own warm beds, and poor Joel's excuses fairly at an end ; then it was, that in the after-dinner pause, about seven, when the clatter of plates and dishes was over, that the ornithological ear of the master of the house, a dabbler in natural history, was struck by a regular and melodious call, the note, as he averred, of a skylark. That a skylark should sing in front of our house, at seven o'clock in a December evening, seemed, to say the least, rather startling. But our ornithologist happening to agree with Mr White, of Selborne, in the opinion that many more birds sing by night than is commonly supposed, and becoming more and more confident of the identity of the note, thought the thing possible ; and not being able to discover any previous notice of the fact, had nearly inserted it, as an original observation, in the Naturalist's Calendar, when running out suddenly one moonlight night, to try for a peep at the nocturnal songster, he caught our friend Joel, whose accomplishments in this line we had never dreamt of, in the act of whistling a summons to his lady love.

For some weeks our demure coquette listened to none but this bird-like wooing ; partly from pride in the conquest ; partly from real preference ; and partly, I believe, from a lurking consciousness that Joel was by no means a lover to be trifled with. Indeed he used to threaten, between jest and earnest, a ducking in the goose-pond opposite, to whoever should presume to

approach his fair intended; and the waters being high and
muddy, and he at all points a formidable rival, most of her
former admirers were content to stay away. At last, however,
she relapsed into her old sin of listening. A neighbouring
farmer gave a ball in his barn, to which both our lovers were
invited and went. Now Harriet loves dancing, and Joel, though
arrayed in a new jacket, and thin cricketing-pumps, would not
dance; he said he could not, but that, as Harriet observes, is
incredible. I agree with her that the gentleman was too fine.
He chose to stand and look on, and laugh, and make laugh, the
whole evening. In the meantime his fair betrothed picked up
a new partner, and a new beau, in the shape of a freshly-arrived
carpenter, a grand martial-looking figure, as tall as a grenadier,
who was recently engaged as foreman to our civil wheeler, and
who, even if he had heard of the denunciation, was of a size and
spirit to set Joel and the goose-pond at defiance—David might
as well have attempted to goose-pond Goliath! He danced
the whole evening with his pretty partner, and afterwards
saw her home; all of which Joel bore with great philosophy.
But the next night he came again; and Joel approaching to
give his own skylark signal, was startled to see another lover
leaning over the wicket, and his faithless mistress standing at
the half-open door listening to the tall carpenter just as com-
placently as she was wont to do to himself. He passed on without speaking, turned down the little lane that leads to Dame
Wheeler's cottage, and in less than two minutes Harriet heard
the love-call sounded at Sally's gate. The effect was instan-
taneous; she discarded the tall carpenter at once and for ever,
locked and bolted the door, and sat down to work or to cry in
the kitchen. She did not cry long. The next night we again
heard the note of the skylark louder and more brilliant than
ever, echoing across our court, and the lovers, the better friends
for their little quarrel, have been as constant as turtle-doves
ever since.

WHEN I had the honour about two years ago of presenting our little village to that multiform and most courteous personage the Public, I hinted I think that it had a trick of standing still, of remaining stationary, unchanged and unimproved in this most changeable and improving world. This habit, whether good or evil, it has retained so pertinaciously, that except that it is two years older, I cannot point out a single alteration which has occurred in our street. I was on the point of paying the inhabitants the same equivocal compliment—and really I almost may—for setting aside the inevitable growth of the younger members of our community, and a few more grey hairs and wrinkles amongst the elder, I see little change. We are the same people, the same generation, neither richer, nor wiser, nor better, nor worse. Some, to be sure, have migrated; and one or two have died; and some—— But we had better step out into the village and look about us.

It is a pleasant lively scene this May morning, with the sun shining so gaily on the irregular rustic dwellings, intermixed with their pretty gardens; a cart and a waggon watering (it would be more correct, perhaps, to say *beering*) at the Rose; Dame Wheeler, with her basket and her brown loaf, just coming from the bake-house; the nymph of the shoe-shop feeding a large family of goslings at the open door—they are very late this year, those noisy little geese; two or three women in high gossip dawdling up the street; Charles North the gardener, with his blue apron and a ladder on his shoulder, walking rapidly by; a cow and a donkey browsing the grass by the wayside; my white greyhound, Mayflower, sitting majestically in front of her own stable; and ducks, chickens, pigs, and children, scattered over all.

A pretty scene! rather more lopping of trees, indeed, and clipping of hedges, along the highroad, than one quite admires; but then that identical turnpike road, my ancient despair, is now so perfect and so beautiful a specimen of Macadamization, that one even learns to like tree-lopping and hedge-clipping for the sake of such smooth ways. It is simply the best road in

England, so says our surveyor, and so say I. The three miles between us and B—— are like a bowling-green. By the way I ought perhaps to mention, as something like change in our outward position, that this little hamlet of ours is much nearer to that illustrious and worshipful town than it used to be. Not that our quiet street hath been guilty of the unbecoming friskiness of skipping from place to place, but that our ancient neighbour, whose suburbs are sprouting forth in all directions, hath made a particularly strong shoot towards us, and threatens some day or other to pay us a visit bodily. The good town has already pushed the turnpike-gate half a mile nearer to us, and is in a fair way to overleap that boundary and build on, till the buildings join ours, as London has done by Hampstead or Kensington. What a strange figure our rude and rustical habitations would cut ranged by the side of some staring red row of newly-erected houses, each as like the other as two drops of water, with courts before and behind, a row of poplars opposite, and a fine new name! How different we should look in our countless variety of nooks and angles, our gardens, and arbours, and lime-trees, and pond! But this union of town and country will hardly happen in my time, let B—— enlarge as it may. We shall certainly lend no assistance, for our boundaries still continue exactly the same.

The first cottage—Ah! here is the post-cart coming up the road at its most respectable rumble, that cart, or rather caravan, which so much resembles a house upon wheels, or a show of the smaller kind at a country fair. It is now crammed full of passengers, the driver just protruding his head and hands out of the vehicle, and the sharp clever boy, who in the occasional absence of his father officiates as deputy, perched like a monkey on the roof. " Any letters to-day ? " And that question, always so interesting, being unsatisfactorily answered, I am at leisure to return to our survey. The first cottage is that erst inhabited by Mr and Mrs H., the retired publican and his good wife. They are gone; I always thought we were too quiet for them; and his eyes being quite recovered, he felt the weariness of idleness more than ever. So they returned to W., where he has taken a comfortable lodging next door to their old and well-frequented inn, the Pie and Parrot, where he has the pleasure every evening of reading the newspaper and abusing the ministers amongst his old customers, himself a customer; as well as of lending his willing aid in waiting and entertaining on fair-days and market-days, at pink-feasts and melon-feasts, to the great solace of mine host, and the no small perplexity of the guests, who, puzzled between the old landlord and the new, hardly know to whom to pay their reckoning, or which to call to account for a bad-tap—a mistake which our sometime neighbour, happier than he has been since he left the *Bar*, particularly enjoys. His successor here is an industrious person, by calling a seedsman, as may be collected by the heaps of pea and bean seed, clover and vetches, piled tier above tier against the window.

The little white cottage down the lane, which stands so prettily, backed by a tall elm wood, has also lost its fair inmate, Sally Wheeler: who finding that Joel continued constant to our pretty Harriet, and was quite out of hope, was suddenly forsaken by the fit of dutifulness which brought her to keep her deaf grandmother company, and returned to service. Dame Wheeler has however a companion, in a widow of her own standing, appointed by the parish to live with, and take care of her. A nice tidy old woman is Dame Shearman—pity that she looks so frumpish—her face seems fixed in one perpetual scold. It was not so when she lived with her sister on the Lea, then she was a light-hearted merry chatterer, whose tongue ran all day long—and that's the reason of her cross look now! Mrs Wheeler is as deaf as a post, and poor Mrs Shearman is pining of a suppression of speech. Fancy what it is for a woman, especially a talking woman, to live without a listener! forced either to hold her peace, or when that becomes impossible, to talk to one to whose sense words are as air! La Trappe is nothing to this tantalization—besides the Trappists were men. No wonder that poor Dame Shearman looks cross.

The Blacksmith's!—no change in that quarter; except a most astonishing growth amongst the children: George looks quite a man, and Betsy, who was just like a blue-eyed doll, with her flaxen curls and her apple-blossom complexion, the prettiest fairy that ever was seen, now walks up to school every morning with her work-bag and her spelling-book, and is really a great girl. They are a fine family from the eldest to the youngest.

The Shoemaker's!—not much to talk of there; no funeral! —and (which disappoints my prediction) no wedding! My pretty neighbour has not yet made her choice. She does wisely to look about her. A belle and an heiress—I dare say she'll have a hundred pounds to her portion—and still in her teens, has some right to be nice. Besides, what would all the mammas, whose babies she nurses, and all the children whom she spoils, do without her? No sparing the Shoemaker's fair daughter! She must not marry yet these half-dozen years!

The shop!—all prosperous, tranquil, and thriving; another little one coming; an idle apprentice run away—more of him anon; and a civil journeyman hired in his room. An excellent

exchange! Jesse is a very agreeable person. He is the politician of the village since we have lost Mr H., and as he goes every day into B—— in his paper cap to carry our country bread, he is sure to bring home the latest intelligence of all sorts, especially of canvassing and electioneering. Jesse has the most complete collection of squibs in the country, and piques himself on his skill in detecting the writers. He will bestow as many guesses, and bring forward as many proofs, on occasion of a hand-bill signed " Fair-Play," or a song subscribed " True-Blue," as ever were given to that abiding riddle, the authorship of Junius—and very likely come as near the mark.

Ah, the dear home! A runaway there too! I may as well tell the story now, although very sorry to have to record so sad an act of delinquency of my clients the boys, as an elopement from our own premises.

Henry Hamilton—that ever a parish boy, offspring of a tailor and a cook-maid, should have an appellation so fitted to the hero of a romance! Henry Hamilton had lived with us for three years and upwards as man of all work, part waterer of my geraniums, sole feeder of May, the general favourite and factotum of the family. Being an orphan with no home but the workhouse, no friend but the overseer, at whose recommendation he was engaged, he seemed to belong to us in an especial manner, to have a more than common claim on protection and kindness. Henry was just the boy to discover and improve this feeling—quick, clever, capable, subtle, and supple; exceedingly agreeable in manner, and pleasant in appearance. He had a light, pliant form, with graceful delicate limbs like a native Indian; a dark but elegant countenance sparkling with expression; and a remarkable variety and versatility of talent. Nothing came amiss to him. In one week he hath been carpenter, blacksmith, painter, tinker, glazier, tailor, cobbler, and wheelwright. These were but a few of his multifarious accomplishments; he would beat Harriet at needlework, and me in gardening. All the parish was in the habit of applying to him on emergency, and I never knew him decline a job in my life. He hath mended a straw bonnet and a smoke-jack, cleaned a clock, constructed a donkey-cart, and dressed a doll.

With all these endowments, Henry was scarcely so good a servant as a duller boy. Besides that he undertook so many things that full half of them were of necessity left unfinished, he was generally to seek when wanted, and after sending a hue-and-cry round the neighbourhood, would be discovered at the blacksmith's or the collar-maker's, intently occupied on some devices of his own. Then he had been praised for invention, till he thought it necessary to display that brilliant quality on all occasions, by which means we, who are exceedingly simple, old-fashioned, matter-of-fact people, were constantly posed by new-fangled novelties, which nobody but the artist could use, or quips and quiddities of no use whatever. Thus we had fastenings for boxes that would not open, and latches for gates that refused to shut, bellows of a new construction that no mortal could blow, and traps that caught fingers instead of rats; May was nearly choked by an improved slip, and my white Camellia killed outright by an infallible wash for insects. Notwithstanding these mishaps, we all liked Henry: his master liked his sportsmanship, his skill and boldness in riding, and the zeal with which he would maintain the honour of his own dogs right or wrong; his mistress liked his civility and good-humour; Harriet felt the value of his alert assistance; and I had a real respect for his resource. In the village he was less a favourite; he looked down upon the other boys, and the men, although amused by his cleverness, looked down upon him.

At last he unfortunately met with a friend of his own age in a clever apprentice, who arrived at our neighbour the baker's from the good town of B——. This youngster, " for shortness called " Bill, was a thorough town boy—you might see at a glance that he had been bred in the streets. He was a bold sturdy lad, with a look compounded of great impudence and a little slyness, and manners, although characterized by the former of these amiable qualities. His voice was a shout, his walk a swagger, and his knock at the door a bounce that threatened to bring the house about our ears. The very first time that I saw him, he was standing before our court with a switch in his hand, with which he was alternately menacing May, who, nothing daunted, returned his attack by an incessant bark, and demolishing a superb crown imperial. Never was a more complete *mauvais sujet*.

This audacious urchin most unfortunately took a great fancy to Henry, which Henry, caught by the dashing assurance of his manner, most unluckily returned. They became friends after the fashion of Orestes and Pylades, or Damon and Pythias, fought for each other, lied for each other, and, finally, ran away with each other. The reason for Bill's evasion was manifest, his conduct having been such that his master had been compelled to threaten him with Bridewell and the treadmill; but why Henry, who, although his invention had latterly taken a de-cided bent towards that branch of ingenuity called mischief, might still have walked quietly out of the street door with a good character in his pocket, should choose to elope from the garret window, is best known to himself. Off they set upward —that is to say, Londonward, the common destination of your country youths who sally forth to try their fortune. Forth they set, and in about a week they were followed by a third runaway, a quiet, simple, modest-looking lad, a sort of hanger-on to the other two, and an apprentice to our worthy neighbour the carpenter. Poor Ned! we were sorry for him; he was of some promise as a cricketer—(by the way, Bill never went near the ground, which I always thought a bad sign)—Ned would really have made a good cricketer, not a brilliant hitter, but an excellent stopper of the ball; one of your safe steady players, whom there is no putting out. Nobody ever dreamt of his running away. We all knew that he was a little idle, and that he was a sort of follower of Bill's—but Ned to decamp! He must have gone out of pure imitation, just as geese waddle into a pond in single file, or as one sheep or pig will follow another through a gap in the hedge—sheer imitation! A notable example of the harm that one town-bred youth will work in a country village! Go he did, and back he is come, poor fellow! thin as a herring, and ragged as a colt, a mere moral to tag a tale withal. He has not had a day's work since he left his good master, nor, to judge from his looks, a sufficient meal. His account of the other two worthies is just what I expected. Henry, after many ups and downs (during one of which he was within half an inch of being a soldier, that is to say, he *did* enlist, and wanted only that much of the standard), is now in a good place, and likely to do well. His *fidus Achates*, Bill, has disappeared from London as he did from the country. No one knows what has become of him. For my own part I never looked for any good from a lad, who, to say nothing of his graver iniquities, kept away from the cricket ground, thrashed my flowers, and tried to thrash May.

The flourishing and well-accustomed Rose Inn has lost its comely mistress, a harmless, blameless, kindly-tempered woman, with a pleasant smile, and a gentle voice, who withered suddenly in the very strength and pride of womanhood, and died lamented by high and low. She is succeeded in the management of that respectable hostelry by two light-footed and light-hearted lasses of twelve and thirteen, who skip about after their good bustling father with an officious civility that the guests find irresistible, and conduct the housekeeping with a frugality and forethought beyond their years.

The white house, with the limes in front, has also lost, though not by death, our good vicar and his charming family. They have taken possession of their own pretty dwelling; and their removal has given me an opportunity of becoming intimately acquainted with all the crooks and turnings, the gates, ponds, and pollards, of the vicarage lane—a walk which, on that event,

I suddenly discovered to be one of the prettiest in the neighbourhood.

Ah! here is Lizzy, half leaning, half riding, on the gate of her own court, looking very demure, and yet quite ripe for a frolic. Lizzy has in some measure outgrown her beauty; which desirable possession does very often run away from a young lady at six years old, and come back again at twelve. I think that such will be the case here. She is still a very nice little girl, quick, clever, active, and useful; goes to school; cooks upon occasion her father's dinner; and is beyond all comparison the handiest little waiting woman in the parish. She is waiting now to speak to her playmate and companion the wheelwright's daughter, who with all her mother's attentive politeness is running down the street with an umbrella and her clogs, to fence their lodger, Mrs Hay, from the ill effects of a summer shower. I think that we have had about a dozen drops of rain, and where they came from no mortal can guess, for there is not a cloud in the sky; but there goes little Mary with a grave civility, a curtsying earnestness, that would be quite amusing in so young a child, if the feeling that dictated the attention were not so good and so real, and the object so respectable.

Mrs Hay is a widow, a slight, delicate, elderly person, in a well-preserved black silk gown, a neat quiet bonnet never in fashion, nor ever wholly out, snow-white stockings, and a handsome grey shawl—her invariable walking costume. She makes no visits; cultivates no acquaintance; and seldom leaves her neat quiet room except to glide into church on a Sunday, and to take a short walk on some fine spring morning. No one knows precisely what Mrs Hay's station has been, but everybody feels that she is an object of interest and respect.

Now up the hill! past the white cottage of the little mason, whiter than ever, for it has just been beautified; past the darker but still prettier dwelling of the lieutenant, mantled with sweetbrier and honeysuckles, and fruit trees of all sorts; one turn to look at the landscape so glowingly bright and green, with its affluence of wood dappled with villages, and gentlemen's seats, the wide spreading town of B—— lying in the distance with its spires and towers, the Thames and the Kennet winding along their lines of light like glittering serpents, and the O—— hills rising beyond;—one glance at that glorious prospect, and here we are at the top of the hill, on the open common, where the air is so fresh and pure, and the sun shines so gaily on the golden furze.

Did I say that there were no alterations in our Village? Could I so utterly forget the great doings on the top of the hill, where by dint of whitening, and sash-windowing, and fresh-dooring, the old ample farm-house has become a very genteel-looking residence? Or the cottage on the common opposite, or rather the two cottages, which have, by a similar transmogrification, been laid into one, and now form, with their new cart-shed, their double garden, and their neat paling, so pretty and comfortable a home for the respectable mistress of the little Village School and her industrious husband? How could I forget that cottage, whose inhabitants I see so often and like so well?

Mr Moore is the greatest market-gardener in the parish; and leads his donkey chaise through the street every summer afternoon, vending fruit and vegetables, and followed by a train of urchins of either sex. Some who walk boldly up to the cart, halfpenny customers, who ask questions and change their minds, balance between the merits of cherries and gooseberries, and gravely calculate under what form of fruit they may get most eating for their money.[1] These are the rich. Others, the shy, who stand aloof, are penniless elves, silent petitioners, who wait about with longing looks, till some child-loving purchaser, or Mr Moore himself, unable to withstand those pleading eyes, flings them a dole, and gives them the double delight of the fruit and the scramble.

The dear cricket ground! Even at this hour there are boys loitering about that beloved scene of evening pastime, not quite playing, but idling and lounging, and looking as if they longed to play. My friend the little Hussar, with his blue jacket and his immovable gravity, is the quietest of the party, and Ben Kirby, youngest brother of Joe (I think I have spoken of Ben before), by far the noisiest. Joe no longer belongs to the boys'

---

[1] It is amusing to see how very early poor children become acquainted with the rate of exchange between the smaller denominations of coin and the commodities —such as cakes, nuts, and gingerbread—which they purchase. No better judge of the currency question than a country brat of three years old. Lizzy, before she could speak plain, was so knowing in cakes and halfpence, that it was a common amusement with the people at the shop where she dealt to try to cheat her, and watch her excessive anger when she detected the imposition. She was sure to find them out, and was never pacified till she had all that was due to her.

side, having been promoted to play with the men; and Ben has succeeded to his post as chief and leader of the youngsters. Joe is a sort of person to make himself happy anywhere, but I suspect that he has not at present gained much pleasure by the exchange. It is always a very equivocal advantage when a person is removed from the first place in one class, to the lowest in the rank just above; and in the present instance poor Joe seems to me to have gained little by his preferment, except the honour of being Fag general to the whole party. His feelings must be something like those of a provincial actor transplanted to the London boards, who finds himself on the scene of his ambition indeed, but playing Richmond instead of Richard, Macduff instead of Macbeth. Joe, however, will doubtless work his way up, and in the meantime Ben fills his abdicated throne with eminent ability.

Jem Eusden, his quondam rival, is lost to the cricket ground altogether. He is gone forth to see the world. An uncle of his mother's, a broker by profession, resident in Shoe-Lane, came into this neighbourhood to attend a great auction, and was so caught by Jem's scholarship, that he carried him off to London and placed him with a hosier in Cheapside, where he is to this hour engaged in tying up gloves and stockings, and carrying out parcels. His grand-uncle describes him as much improved by the removal: and his own letters to Ben (for since they have been parted they are become great friends) confirm the assertion. He writes by every opportunity, full as often, I should think, as once a quarter: and his letters give by far the best accounts of the Lord Mayor's day, as well as of the dwarfs, giants, and other monsters on show in London, of any that arrive in these parts. He is critical on the Christmas Panto-mimes, descriptive on the Panoramas, and his narrative on the death of the elephant (whose remains his good kinsman the broker took him to visit) was so pathetic that it made the whole village cry. All the common is in admiration of Jem's genius, always excepting his friend Ben Kirby, who laughs at every-thing, even his correspondent's letters, and hath been heard to insinuate that the most eloquent morceaux are " bits out of newspapers." Ben is a shrewd wag and a knowing; but in this instance I think that he is mistaken. I hold Jem's flights for original, and suspect that the young gentleman will turn out literary.

JACK HATCH

I PIQUE myself on knowing by sight, and by name, almost every man and boy in our parish, from eight years old to eighty—I cannot say quite so much for the women. They—the elder of them at least—are more within doors, more hidden. One does not meet them in the fields and highways; their duties are close housekeepers, and live under cover. The girls, to be sure, are often enough in sight, " true creatures of the element," basking in the sun, racing in the wind, rolling in the dust, dabbling in the water—hardier, dirtier, noisier, more sturdy defiers of heat, and cold, and wet, than boys themselves. One sees them quite often enough to know them; but then the little elves alter so much at every step of their approach to womanhood, that recognition becomes difficult, if not impossible. It is not merely growing—boys grow—it is positive, perplexing, and perpetual change: a butterfly hath not undergone more transmogrifications in its progress through this life, than a village belle in her arrival at the age of seventeen.

The first appearance of the little lass is something after the manner of a caterpillar, crawling and creeping upon the grass, set down to roll by some tired little nurse of an elder sister, or mother with her hands full. There it lies—a fat, boneless, rosy piece of health, aspiring to the accomplishments of walking and talking; stretching its chubby limbs; scrambling and sprawling; laughing and roaring; there it sits, in all the dignity of the baby, adorned in a pink-checked frock, a blue spotted pinafore, and a little white cap, tolerably clean, and quite whole. One is forced to ask if it be boy or girl; for these hardy country rogues are all alike, open-eyed, and weather-stained, and nothing fearing. There is no more mark of sex in the countenance than in the dress.

In the next stage, dirt-incrusted enough to pass for the chrysalis, if it were not so very unquiet, the gender remains equally uncertain. It is a fine, stout, curly-pated creature of three or four, playing and rolling about, amongst grass or mud, all day long; shouting, jumping, screeching—the happiest compound of noise and idleness, rags and rebellion, that ever trod the earth.

Then comes a sun-burnt gipsy of six, beginning to grow tall and thin, and to find the cares of the world gathering about her; with a pitcher in one hand, a mop in the other, an old straw bonnet of ambiguous shape, half hiding her tangled hair; a tattered stuff petticoat, once green, hanging below an equally tattered cotton frock, once purple; her longing eyes fixed on a game of baseball at the corner of the green, till she reaches the cottage door, flings down the mop and pitcher, and darts off to her companions, quite regardless of the storm of scolding with which the mother follows her run-away steps.

So the world wags till ten; then the little damsel gets admission to the charity school, and trips mincingly thither every morning, dressed in the old-fashioned blue gown, and white cap, and tippet, and bib and apron of that primitive institution, looking as demure as a Nun, and as tidy; her thoughts fixed on button-holes and spelling-books—those ensigns of promotion; despising dirt and baseballs, and all their joys.

Then at twelve the little lass comes home again, uncapped, untippeted, unschooled; brown as a berry, wild as a colt, busy as a bee—working in the fields, digging in the garden, frying rashers, boiling potatoes, shelling beans, darning stockings, nursing children, feeding pigs;—all these employments varied by occasional fits of romping and flirting, and idle play, according as the nascent coquetry, or the lurking love of sport, happens to preponderate; merry, and pretty, and good with all her little faults. It would be well if a country girl could stand at thirteen. Then she is charming. But the clock will move forward, and at fourteen she gets a service in a neighbouring town; and her next appearance is in the perfection of the butterfly state, fluttering, glittering, inconstant, vain—the gayest and gaudiest insect that ever skimmed over a village green. And this is the true progress of a rustic beauty, the average lot of our country girls; so they spring up, flourish, change, and disappear. Some indeed marry and fix amongst us, and then ensues another set of changes, rather more gradual perhaps, but quite as sure, till grey hairs, wrinkles, and linsey-woolsey wind up the picture.

All this is beside the purpose. If woman be a mutable creature, man is not. The wearers of smock-frocks, in spite of the sameness of the uniform, are almost as easily distinguished by an interested eye, as a flock of sheep by the shepherd, or a pack of hounds by the huntsman: or, to come to less affronting similes, the members of the House of Commons by the Speaker, or the gentlemen of the bar by the Lord Chief Justice. There is very little change in them from early boyhood. " The child is father to the man " in more senses than one. There is a constancy about them; they keep the same faces, however ugly; the same habits, however strange; the same fashions, however unfashionable; they are in nothing new-fangled. Tom Coper, for instance, man and boy, is and has been addicted to posies— from the first polyanthus to the last china rose, he has always a nosegay in his button-hole; George Simmons may be known a mile off, by an eternal red waistcoat; Jem Tanner, summer and winter, by the smartest of all smart straw hats; and Joel Brent, from the day that he left off petticoats, has always, in every dress and every situation, looked like a study for a painter—no mistaking him. Yes! I know every man and boy of note in the parish, with one exception—one most singular exception, which " haunts, and startles, and waylays " me at every turn. I do not know, and I begin to fear that I never shall know, Jack Hatch.

The first time I had occasion to hear of this worthy was on a most melancholy occurrence. We have lost—I do not like to talk about it, but I cannot tell my story without—we have lost a cricket match, been beaten, and soundly too, by the men of Beech-hill, a neighbouring parish. How this accident happened, I cannot very well tell; the melancholy fact is sufficient. The men of Beech-hill, famous players, in whose families cricket is an hereditary accomplishment, challenged and beat us. After our defeat, we began to comfort ourselves by endeavouring to discover how this misfortune could possibly have befallen. Every one that has ever had a cold must have experienced the great consolation that is derived from puzzling out the particular act of imprudence from which it sprang, and we, on the same principle, found our affliction somewhat mitigated by the endeavour to trace it to its source. One laid the catastrophe to the wind—a very common scapegoat in the catarrhal calamity— which had, as it were, played us booty, carrying our adversaries' balls right and ours wrong; another laid it to a certain catch missed by Tom Willis, by which means Farmer Thackum, the pride and glory of the Beech-hillers, had two innings; a third to the aforesaid Thackum's remarkable manner of bowling, which is circular, so to say, that is, after taking aim, he makes a sort of chassée on one side, before he delivers his ball, which pantomimic motion had a great effect on the nerves of our eleven, unused to such quadrilling; a fourth imputed our defeat to the over-civility of our umpire, George Gosseltine, a sleek, smooth, silky, soft-spoken person, who stood with his little wand under his arm, smiling through all our disasters—the very image of peace and good-humour; whilst their umpire, Bob Coxe, a roystering, roaring, bullying blade, bounced, and hectored, and blustered from his wicket, with the voice of a twelve-pounder; the fifth assented to this opinion, with some extension, asserting that the universal impudence of their side took advantage of the meekness and modesty of ours (N.B. it never occurred to our modesty, that they might be the best players), which flattering persuasion appeared likely to prevail, in fault of a better, when all on a sudden the true reason of our defeat seemed to burst at once from half a dozen voices, re-echoed like a chorus by all the others—" It was entirely owing to the want of Jack Hatch! How could we think of playing without Jack Hatch!"

This was the first I heard of him. My inquiries as to this great player were received with utter astonishment. " Who is Jack?" " Not know Jack Hatch!" There was no end of the wonder—" not to know him, argued myself unknown." " Jack Hatch—the best cricketer in the parish, in the county, in the country! Jack Hatch, who had got seven notches at one hit! Jack Hatch, who had trolled, and caught out a whole eleven! Jack Hatch, who, besides these marvellous gifts in cricket, was the best bowler and the best musician in the hundred—could dance a hornpipe and a minuet, sing a whole song-book, bark like a dog, mew like a cat, crow like a cock, and go through Punch from beginning to end! Not know Jack Hatch!"

Half ashamed of my non-acquaintance with this Admirable Crichton of rural accomplishments, I determined to find him out as soon as possible, and I have been looking for him more or less ever since.

The cricket ground and the bowling-green were of course the first places of search; but he was always just gone, or not come, or he was there yesterday, or he is expected to-morrow—a to-morrow which, as far as I am concerned, never arrives;—the stars were against me. Then I directed my attention to his other acquirements; and once followed a ballad-singer half a mile,

K

who turned out to be a strapping woman in a man's great coat; and another time pierced a whole mob of urchins to get at a capital Punch—when behold it was the genuine man of puppets, the true squeakery, the "real Simon Pure," and Jack was as much to seek as ever.

At last I thought that I had actually caught him, and on his own peculiar field, the cricket ground. We abound in rustic fun, and good humour, and of course in nicknames. A certain senior of fifty, or thereabout, for instance, of very juvenile habits and inclinations, who plays at ball, and marbles, and cricket with all the boys in the parish, and joins a kind merry buoyant heart to an aspect somewhat rough and careworn, has no other appellation that ever I heard but "Uncle"; I don't think, if by any strange chance he were called by it, that he would know his own name. On the other hand, a little stunted pragmatical urchin, son and heir of Dick Jones, an absolute old man cut shorter, so slow, and stiff, and sturdy, and wordy, passes universally by the title of "Grandfather"—I have not the least notion that he would answer to Dick. Also a slim, grim-looking, white-headed lad, whose hair is bleached, and his skin browned by the sun, till he is as hideous as an Indian idol, goes, good lack! by the pastoral misnomer of the "Gentle Shepherd." Oh manes of Allan Ramsay! the Gentle Shepherd!

Another youth, regular at cricket, but never seen except then, of unknown parish, and parentage, and singular uncouthness of person, dress, and demeanour, rough as a badger, ragged as a colt, and sour as verjuice, was known, far more appropriately, by the cognomen of "Oddity." Him, in my secret soul, I pitched on for Jack Hatch. In the first place, as I had in the one case a man without a name, and in the other a name without a man, to have found these component parts of individuality meet in the same person, to have made the man to fit the name, and the name fit the man, would have been as pretty a way of solving two enigmas at once, as hath been heard of since Œdipus his day. But besides the obvious convenience and suitability of this belief, I had divers other corroborating reasons. Oddity was young, so was Jack; Oddity came up the hill from leaward, so must Jack; Oddity was a capital cricketer, so was Jack; Oddity did not play in our unlucky Beech-hill match, neither did Jack; and last of all, Oddity's name was Jack, a fact I was fortunate enough to ascertain from a pretty damsel who walked up with him to the ground one evening, and who, on seeing him bowl out Tom Coper, could not help exclaiming in soliloquy, as she stood a few yards behind us, looking on with all her heart, " Well done, Jack ! " That moment built up all my hopes ; the next knocked them down. I thought I had clutched him, but willing to make assurance doubly sure, I turned to my pretty neighbour (Jack Hatch too had a sweetheart), and said in a tone, half affirmative, half interrogatory, " That young man who plays so well is Jack Hatch ? "—" No, ma'am, Jack Bolton ! " and Jack Hatch remained still a sound, a name, a mockery.

Well ! at last I ceased to look for him, and might possibly have forgotten my curiosity, had not every week produced some circumstance to relumine that active female passion.

I seemed beset by his name, and his presence, invisibly as it were. Will o' the wisp is nothing to him ; Puck, in that famous Midsummer Dream, was a quiet goblin compared to Jack Hatch. He haunts one in dark places. The fiddler, whose merry tones come ringing across the orchard in a winter's night from Farmer White's barn, setting the whole village a dancing, is Jack Hatch. The whistler, who trudges homeward at dusk up Kibe's lanes, out-piping the nightingale, in her own month of May, is Jack Hatch. And the indefatigable learner of the bassoon, whose drone, all last harvest, might be heard in the twilight, issuing from the sexton's dwelling on the Little Lea, " making night hideous," that iniquitous practiser is Jack Hatch.

The name meets me all manner of ways. I have seen it in the newspaper for a prize of pinks ; and on the back of a warrant on the charge of poaching—N.B. the constable had my luck, and could not find the culprit, otherwise I might have had some chance of seeing him on that occasion. Things the most remote and discrepant issue in Jack Hatch. He caught Dame Wheeler's squirrel ; the Magpie at the Rose owes to him the half-dozen phrases with which he astounds and delights the passers-by ; the very dog Tero—an animal of singular habits, who sojourns occasionally at half the houses in the village, making each his home till he is affronted—Tero himself, best and ugliest of finders—a mongrel compounded of terrier, cur, and spaniel— Tero, most remarkable of ugly dogs, inasmuch as he constantly squints, and commonly goes on three legs, holding up first one, and then the other, out of a sort of quadrupedal economy to ease those useful members—Tero himself is said to belong of right and origin to Jack Hatch.

Everywhere that name meets me. 'Twas but a few weeks ago that I heard him asked in church, and a day or two afterwards I saw the tail of the wedding procession, the little lame clerk handing the bridemaid, and a girl from the Rose running after them with pipes, passing by our house. Nay, this very morning, some one was speaking—Dead! what dead? Jack Hatch dead? —a name, a shadow, a Jack o' lantern! Can Jack Hatch die? Hath he the property of mortality? Can the bell toll for him? Yes! there is the coffin and the pall—all that I shall ever see of him is there!—There are his comrades following in decent sorrow—and the poor pretty bride, leaning on the little clerk.— My search is over—Jack Hatch is dead!

DOCTOR TUBB

EVERY country village has its doctor. I allude to that particular department of the medical world, which is neither physician, nor surgeon, nor apothecary, although it unites the offices of all three; which is sometimes an old man, and sometimes an old woman, but generally an oracle, and always (with reverence be it spoken) a quack. Our village, which is remarkably rich in functionaries adorned with the true official qualities, could hardly be without so essential a personage. Accordingly we have a quack of the highest and most extended reputation in the person of Doctor Tubb, inventor and compounder of medicines, bleeder, shaver, and physicker of man and beast.

How this accomplished barber-surgeon came by his fame I do not very well know; his skill he inherited (as I have been told) in the female line, from his great-aunt Bridget, who was herself the first practitioner of the day, the wise woman of the village, and bequeathed to this favourite nephew her blessing, Culpepper's Herbal, a famous salve for cuts and chilblains, and a still. This legacy decided his fate. A man who possessed an herbal and could read it without much spelling, who had a still and could use it, had already the great requisites for his calling. He was also blest with a natural endowment which I take to be at least equally essential to the success of quackery of any sort, especially of medical quackery; namely, a prodigious stock of impudence. Molière's hero—who having had the ill-luck to place the heart on the wrong side (I mean the right), and being reminded of his mistake, says coolly, " nous avons changé tout cela "—is modesty itself compared with the brazen front of Doctor Tubb. And it tells accordingly. Patients come to him from far and near; he is the celebrated person (*l'homme marquant*) of the place. I myself have heard of him all my life as a distinguished character, although all our personal acquaintance is of a comparatively recent date, and began in a manner sufficiently singular and characteristic.

On taking possession of our present abode, about four years

ago, we found our garden, and all the gardens of the straggling
village street in which it is situated, filled, peopled, infested by
a beautiful flower, which grew in such profusion, and was so
difficult to keep under, that (poor pretty thing!) instead of
being admired and cherished and watered and supported, as it
well deserves to be, and would be if it were rare, it is disregarded,
affronted, maltreated, cut down, pulled up, hoed out, like a
weed. I do not know the name of this elegant plant, nor have I
met with any one who does; we call it the Spicer, after an old
naval officer who once inhabited the white house just above,
and, according to tradition, first brought the seed from foreign
parts. It is a sort of large veronica, with a profusion of white
gauzy flowers streaked with red, like the apple blossom.
Strangers admire it prodigiously; and so do I—everywhere
but in my own garden.

I never saw anything prettier than a whole bed of these
spicers, which had clothed the top of a large heap of earth
belonging to our little mason by the roadside. Whether the
wind had carried the light seed from his garden, or it had been
thrown out in the mould, none could tell; but there grew the
plants as thick and close as grass in a meadow, and covered with
delicate red and white blossoms like a fairy orchard. I never
passed without stopping to look at them; and, however accustomed to the work of extirpation in my own territories, I was
one day half-shocked to see a man, his pockets stuffed with the
plants, two huge bundles under each arm, and still tugging away
root and branch. " Poor pretty flower," thought I, " not even
suffered to enjoy the waste by the roadside! chased from the
very common of nature, where the thistle and the nettle may
spread and flourish! Poor despised flower! " This devastation
did not, however, as I soon found, proceed from disrespect; the
spicer-gatherer being engaged in sniffing with visible satisfaction
to the leaves and stalks of the plant, which (although the blossom
is wholly scentless) emit when bruised a very unpleasant odour.
" It has a fine venomous smell," quoth he in soliloquy, " and
will certainly when stilled be good for something or other."
This was my first sight of Doctor Tubb.

We have frequently met since, and are now well acquainted,
although the worthy experimentalist considers me as a rival
practitioner, an interloper, and hates me accordingly. He has
very little cause. My quackery—for I plead guilty to a little of

that aptness to offer counsel in very plain and common cases, which those who live much among poor people, and feel an unaffected interest in their health and comfort, can hardly help —my quackery, being mostly of the cautious, preventive, safe side, common-sense order, stands no chance against the boldness and decision of his all-promising ignorance. He says, Do! I say, Do not! He deals in *stimuli*, I in sedatives; I give medicine, he gives cordial waters. Alack! alack! when could a dose of rhubarb, even although reinforced by a dole of good broth, compete with a draught of peppermint, a licensed dram? No! no! Doctor Tubb has no cause to fear my practice.

The only patient I ever won from the worthy empiric was his own wife, who had languished under his prescriptions for three mortal years, and at last stole down in the dusk of the evening to hold a private consultation with me. I was not very willing to invade the doctor's territories in my own person, and really feared to undertake a case which had proved so obstinate; I therefore offered her a ticket to the B. dispensary, an excellent charity, which has rescued many a victim from the clutches of our herbalist. But she said that her husband would never forgive such an affront to his skill, he having an especial aversion to the dispensary and its excellent medical staff, whom he was wont to call " book-doctors "; so that wise measure was perforce abandoned. My next suggestion was more to her taste; I counselled her to " throw physic to the dogs "; she did so, and by the end of the week she was another woman. I never saw such a cure. Her husband never made such a one in all the course of his practice. By the simple expedient of throwing away his decoctions, she is become as strong and as hearty as I am. N.B. for fear of misconstruction, it is proper to add, that I do not in the least accuse or suspect the worthy doctor of wishing to get rid of his wife—God forbid! He is a tolerable husband, as times go, and performs no murders but in the way of his profession: indeed, I think he is glad that his wife should be well again; yet he cannot quite forgive the cause of the cure, and continues boldly to assert, in all companies, that it was a newly discovered fomentation of *yarbs*, applied to her by himself about a month before, which produced this surprising recovery; and I really believe that he thinks so. One secret of the implicit confidence which he inspires, is that triumphant reliance on his own infallibility with which he is possessed—the secret perhaps of all creators of enthusiasm, from Mahomet and Cromwell to the

> Prevailing poet, whose undoubting mind
> Believ'd the magic wonders that he sang.

As if to make some amends to this prescriber-general for the patient of whom I had deprived him, I was once induced to seek his services medically, or rather surgically, for one of my own family—for no less a person than May, poor pretty May! One November evening, her master being on a coursing visit in Oxfordshire, and May having been left behind as too much fatigued with a recent hard day's work to stand a long dirty journey (note that a greyhound, besides being exceedingly susceptible of bad weather and watery ways, is a worse traveller than any other dog that breathes; a miserable little pug, or a lady's lap-dog, would, in a progress of fifty miles, tire down the slayer of hares and outrunner of racehorses)—May being, as I said, left behind slightly indisposed, the boy who had the care of her, no less a person than the runaway Henry, came suddenly into the parlour to tell me that she was dying. Now May is not only my pet but the pet of the whole house, so that the news spread universal consternation; there was a sudden rush of the female world to the stable, and a general feeling that Henry was right, when poor May was discovered stretched at full length in a stall, with no other sign of life than a tremendous and visible pulsation of the arteries about her chest—you might almost hear the poor heart beat, so violent was the action. " Bleeding! "— " She must be bled! " burst simultaneously from two of our corps; and immediately her body-servant the boy, who stood compromising his dignity by a very unmanly shower of tears, vanished, and reappeared in a few seconds, dragging Doctor Tubb by the skirts, who, as it was Saturday night, was exercising his tonsorial functions in the tap-room of the Rose, where he is accustomed to operate hebdominally on half the beards of the parish.

The doctor made his entry apparently with considerable reluctance, enacting for the first and last time in his life the part of *Le Médecin malgré lui*. He held his razor in one hand and a shaving brush in the other, whilst a barber's apron was tied round the shabby, rusty, out-at-elbow, second-hand black coat, renewed once in three years, and the still shabbier black breeches, of which his costume usually consists. In spite of my seeming, as I really was, glad to see him, a compliment which from me had at least the charm of novelty—in spite of a very gracious reception, I never saw the man of medicine look more completely astray. He has a pale, meagre, cadaverous face at all times, and a long lank body that seems as if he fed upon his own physic (although it is well known that gin, sheer gin, of which he is by no means sparing, is the only distilled water that finds its way down his throat)—but on this night, between fright—for Henry had taken possession of him without even explaining his errand—and shame to be dragged into my presence whilst bearing the *insignia* of the least dignified of his professions, his very wig, the identical brown scratch, which he wears by way of looking professional, actually stood on end. He was followed by a miscellaneous procession of assistants, very kind, very curious, and very troublesome, from that noisy neighbour of ours, the well-frequented Rose inn. First marched mine host, red waistcoated and jolly as usual, bearing a huge foaming pewter pot of double X, a sovereign cure for all sublunary ills, and lighted by the limping hostler, who tried in vain to keep pace with the swift stride of his master, and held at arm's length before him a smoky horn lantern, which might well be called dark. Next tripped Miss Phœbe (this misadventure happened before the grand event of her marriage with the patten-maker), with a flaring candle in one hand and a glass of cherry brandy, reserved by her mother for grand occasions, in the other—*autre remède!* Then followed the motley crew of the tap-room, among whom figured my friend Joel, with a woman's apron tied round his neck, and his chin covered with lather, he having been the identical customer—the very shavee, whose beard happened to be under discussion when the unfortunate interruption occurred.

After the bustle and alarm had in some measure subsided, the doctor marched up gravely to poor May, who had taken no sort of notice of the uproar.

" She must be bled ! " quoth I.

" She must be fomented and physicked ! " quoth the doctor ! and he immediately produced from either pocket a huge bundle of dried herbs (perhaps the identical venomous-smelling spicer) which he gave to Miss Phœbe to make into a decoction *secundum artem,* and a huge horse-ball which he proceeded to divide into bolusses;—think of giving a horse-ball to my May!—" She must be bled immediately! " said I.

" She must not! " replied the doctor.

" You shall bleed her! " cried Henry.

" I won't! " rejoined the doctor. " She shall be fo "—*mented* he would have added; but her faithful attendant, thoroughly enraged, screamed out " She sha'n't! " and a regular scolding match ensued, during which both parties entirely lost sight of the poor patient, and mine host of the Rose had very nearly succeeded in administering his specific—the double X, which would doubtless have been as fatal as any prescription of licentiate or quack. The worthy landlord had actually forced open her jaws, and was about to pour in the liquor, when I luckily interposed in time to give the ale a more natural direction down his own throat, which was almost as well accustomed to such potations as that of Boniface. He was not at all offended at my rejection of his kindness, but drank to my health and May's recovery with equal good-will.

In the meantime the tumult was ended by my friend the cricketer, who, seeing the turn which things were taking, and quite regardless of his own plight, ran down the village to the lea, to fetch another friend of mine, an old gamekeeper, who set us all to rights in a moment, cleared the stable of the curious impertinents, flung the horse-ball on the dung-hill and the decoction into the pond, bled poor May, and turned out the doctor; after which, it is almost needless to say that the patient recovered.

THE OLD GIPSY

W E have few gipsies in our neighbourhood. In spite of
our tempting green lanes, our woody dells and heathy
commons, the rogues don't take to us. I am afraid that we are
too civilized, too cautious; that our sheep-folds are too closely
watched; our barn-yards too well guarded; our geese and
ducks too fastly penned; our chickens too securely locked up;
our little pigs too safe in their sty; our game too scarce; our
laundresses too careful. In short, we are too little primitive:
we have a snug brood of vagabonds and poachers of our own,
to say nothing of their regular followers, constables and justices
of the peace; we have stocks in the village, and a treadmill in
the next town; and therefore we go gipsyless—a misfortune of
which every landscape painter, and every lover of that living
landscape, the country, can appreciate the extent. There is
nothing under the sun that harmonizes so well with nature,
especially in her woodland recesses, as that picturesque people,
who are, so to say, the wild genus—the pheasants and roebucks
of the human race.

Sometimes, indeed, we used to see a gipsy procession passing
along the common, like an eastern caravan, men, women, and
children, donkeys and dogs; and sometimes a patch of bare
earth, strewed with ashes and surrounded with scathed turf, on
the broad green margin of some cross-road, would give token
of a gipsy halt; but a regular gipsy encampment has always
been so rare an event, that I was equally surprised and delighted
to meet with one in the course of my walks last autumn, particularly as the party was of the most innocent description, quite
free from those tall, dark, lean, Spanish-looking men, who it
must be confessed, with all my predilection for the caste, are
rather startling to meet when alone in an unfrequented path:
and a path more solitary than that into which the beauty of
a bright October morning had tempted me could not well be
imagined.

Branching off from the highroad, a little below our village,
runs a wide green lane, bordered on either side by a row of
young oaks and beeches just within the hedge, forming an

avenue, in which, on a summer afternoon, you may see the squirrels disporting from tree to tree, whilst the rooks, their fellow denizens, are wheeling in noisy circles over their heads. The fields sink gently down on each side, so that, being the bottom of a natural winding valley, and crossed by many little hills and rivulets, the turf exhibits even in the dryest summers an emerald verdure. Scarcely any one passes the end of that lane without wishing to turn into it; but the way is in some sort dangerous and difficult for foot passengers, because the brooklets which intersect it are in many instances bridgeless, and in others bestridden by planks so decayed, that it were rashness to pass them; and the nature of the ground, treacherous and boggy, and in many places as unstable as water, render it for carriages wholly impracticable.

I however, who do not dislike a little difficulty where there is no absolute danger, and who am moreover almost as familiar with the one only safe track as the heifers who graze there, sometimes venture along this seldom-trodden path, which terminates, at the end of a mile and a half, in a spot of singular beauty. The hills become abrupt and woody, the cultivated enclosures cease, and the long narrow valley ends in a little green, bordered on one side by a fine old park, whose mossy paling, overhung with thorns and hollies, comes sweeping round it, to meet the rich coppices which clothe the opposite acclivity. Just under the high and irregular paling, shaded by the birches and sycamores of the park, and by the venerable oaks which are scattered irregularly on the green, is a dark deep pool, whose broken banks, crowned with fern and wreathed with brier and bramble, have an air of wildness and grandeur that might have suited the pencil of Salvator Rosa.

In this lonely place (for the mansion to which the park belongs has long been uninhabited) I first saw our gipsies. They had pitched their tent under one of the oak-trees, perhaps from a certain dim sense of natural beauty, which those who live with nature in the fields are seldom totally without; perhaps because the neighbourhood of the coppices, and of the deserted hall, was favourable to the acquisition of game, and of the little fuel which their hardy habits required. The party consisted only of four—an old crone, in a tattered red cloak and black bonnet, who was stooping over a kettle, of which the contents were probably as savoury as that of Meg Merrilies, renowned

in story; a pretty black-eyed girl, at work under the trees; a
sun-burnt urchin of eight or nine, collecting sticks and dead
leaves to feed their out-of-door fire, and a slender lad two or
three years older, who lay basking in the sun, with a couple of
shabby dogs, of the sort called mongrel, in all the joy of idleness,
whilst a grave patient donkey stood grazing hard-by. It was a
pretty picture, with its soft autumnal sky, its rich woodiness, its
sunshine, its verdure, the light smoke curling from the fire, and
the group disposed around it so harmless, poor outcasts! and so
happy—a beautiful picture! I stood gazing on it till I was half

ashamed to look longer, and came away half afraid that they
should depart before I could see them again.

This fear I soon found to be groundless. The old gipsy was
a celebrated fortune-teller, and the post having been so long
vacant, she could not have brought her talents to a better
market. The whole village rang with the predictions of this
modern Cassandra—unlike her Trojan predecessor, inasmuch
as her prophecies were never of evil. I myself could not help
admiring the real cleverness, the genuine gipsy tact with which
she adapted her foretellings to the age, the habits, and the known
desires and circumstances of her clients.

To our little pet, Lizzy, for instance, a damsel of seven, she
predicted a fairing; to Ben Kirby, a youth of thirteen, head
batter of the boys, a new cricket-ball; to Ben's sister Lucy, a
girl some three years his senior, and just promoted to that
ensign of womanhood a cap, she promised a pink top-knot;
whilst for Miss Sophia Matthews, our old-maidish schoolmistress
who would be heartily glad to be a girl again, she foresaw one

handsome husband, and for the smart widow Simmons, two. These were the least of her triumphs. George Davis, the dashing young farmer of the hill-house, a gay sportsman, who scoffed at fortune-tellers and matrimony, consulted her as to whose greyhound would win the courser's cup at the beacon meeting: to which she replied that she did not know to whom the dog would belong, but that the winner of the cup would be a white greyhound, with one blue ear, and a spot on its side, being an exact description of Mr George Davis's favourite Helen, who followed her master's steps like his shadow, and was standing behind him at this very instant. This prediction gained our gipsy half a crown. And Master Welles—the thriving thrifty yeoman of the Lea—she managed to win sixpence from his hard honest frugal hand, by a prophecy that his old brood mare, called Blackfoot, should bring forth twins. And Ned the blacksmith, who was known to court the tall nursemaid at the mill— she got a shilling from Ned, simply by assuring him that his wife should have the longest coffin that ever was made in our wheelwright's shop. A most tempting prediction! ingeniously combining the prospect of winning and of surviving the lady of his heart—a promise equally adapted to the hot and cold fits of that ague called love; lightening the fetters of wedlock; uniting in a breath the bridegroom and the widower. Ned was the best pleased of all her customers, and enforced his suit with such vigour, that he and the fair giantess were asked in church the next Sunday, and married at the fortnight's end.

No wonder that all the world—that is to say, all our world— were crazy to have their fortunes told—to enjoy the pleasure of hearing from such undoubted authority, that what they wished to be should be. Amongst the most eager to take a peep into futurity, was our pretty maid Harriet, although her desire took the not unusual form of disclamation—" nothing should induce her to have her fortune told, nothing upon earth! She never thought of the gipsy, not she! " and, to prove the fact, she said so at least twenty times a day. Now Harriet's fortune seemed told already; her destiny was fixed. She, the belle of the village, was engaged, as everybody knows, to our village beau, Joel Brent; they were only waiting for a little more money to marry; and as Joel was already head carter to our head farmer, and had some prospect of a bailiff's place, their union did not appear very distant. But Harriet, besides being a beauty, was a coquette, and her affection for her betrothed did not interfere with certain flirtations which came in like Isabella, " by-the-bye," and occasionally cast a shadow of coolness between the lovers, which, however, Joel's cleverness and good-humour generally contrived to chase away. There had probably been a little fracas in the present instance, for at the end of one of her daily professions of unfaith in gipsies and their predictions, she added, " that none but fools did believe them; that Joel had had his fortune told, and wanted to treat her to a prophecy—but she was not such a simpleton."

About an hour after the delivery of this speech, I happened, in tying up a chrysanthemum, to go to our wood-yard for a stick of proper dimensions, and there, enclosed between the faggot-pile and the coal-shed, stood the gipsy, in the very act of palmistry, conning the lines of fate in Harriet's hand. Never was a stronger contrast than that between the old withered sibyl, dark as an Egyptian, with bright laughing eyes, and an expression of keen humour under all her affected solemnity, and our village beauty, tall, and plump, and fair, blooming as a rose, and simple as a dove. She was listening too intently to see me, but the fortune-teller did, and stopped so suddenly that her attention was awakened, and the intruder discovered.

Harriet at first meditated a denial. She called up a pretty innocent unconcerned look; answered my silence (for I never spoke a word) by muttering something about " coals for the parlour "; and catching up my new-painted green watering-pot instead of the coal-scuttle, began filling it with all her might, to the unspeakable discomfiture of that useful utensil, on which the dingy dust stuck like birdlime—and of her own clean apron, which exhibited a curious interchange of black and green on a white ground. During the process of filling the watering-pot, Harriet made divers signs to the gipsy to decamp. The old sibyl, however, budged not a foot, influenced probably by two reasons, one, the hope of securing a customer in the newcomer, whose appearance is generally, I am afraid, the very reverse of dignified, rather merry than wise; the other, a genuine fear of passing through the yard-gate, on the outside of which a much more imposing person, my greyhound Mayflower, who has a sort of beadle instinct anent drunkards and pilferers, and disorderly persons of all sorts, stood barking most furiously.

This instinct is one of May's remarkable qualities. Dogs are

all, more or less, physiognomists, and commonly pretty determined aristocrats, fond of the fine and averse to the shabby,
distinguishing, with a nice accuracy, the master castes from the
pariahs of the world. But May's power of perception is another
matter, more, as it were, moral. She has no objection to honest
rags; can away with dirt, or age, or ugliness, or any such
accident, and, except just at home, makes no distinction between kitchen and parlour. Her intuition points entirely to
the race of people commonly called suspicious, on whom she
pounces at a glance. What a constable she would have made!
What a jewel of a thief-taker! Pity that those four feet should
stand in the way of her preferment! she might have risen to
be a Bow-street officer. As it is we make the gift useful in a
small way. In the matter of hiring and marketing the whole
village likes to consult May. Many a chap has stared when she
has been whistled up to give her opinion as to his honesty; and
many a pig bargain has gone off on her veto. Our neighbour,
mine host of the Rose, used constantly to follow her judgment
in the selection of his lodgers. His house was never so orderly
as when under her government. At last he found out that she
abhorred tipplers as well as thieves—indeed, she actually
barked away three of his best customers: and he left off appealing to her sagacity, since which he has, at different times, lost
three silver spoons and a leg of mutton. With every one else
May is an oracle. Not only in the case of wayfarers and
vagrants, but amongst our own people, her fancies are quite a
touchstone. A certain hump-backed cobbler, for instance—
May cannot abide him, and I don't think he has had so much
as a job of heel-piecing to do since her dislike became public.
She really took away his character.

Longer than I have taken to relate Mayflower's accomplishments stood we, like the folks in the *Critic*, at a deadlock; May,
who probably regarded the gipsy as a sort of rival, an interloper
on her oracular domain, barking with the voice of a lioness—the
gipsy trying to persuade me into having my fortune told—and
I endeavouring to prevail on May to let the gipsy pass. Both
attempts were unsuccessful: and the fair consulter of destiny,
who had by this time recovered from the shame of her detection,
extricated us from our dilemma by smuggling the old woman
away through the house.

Of course Harriet was exposed to some raillery, and a good

deal of questioning about her future fate, as to which she preserved an obstinate, but evidently satisfied silence. At the end
of three days, however—my readers are, I hope, learned enough
in gipsy lore to know that, unless kept secret for three entire
days, no prediction can come true—at the end of three days,
when all the family except herself had forgotten the story, our
pretty soubrette, half bursting with the long retention, took the
opportunity of lacing on my new half-boots to reveal the prophecy. " She was to see within the week, and this was Saturday,
the young man, the real young man, whom she was to marry."
—" Why, Harriet, you know poor Joel."—" Joel, indeed! the
gipsy said that the young man, the real young man, was to ride
up to the house drest in a dark great-coat (and Joel never
wore a great-coat in his life—all the world knew that he wore
smock-frocks and jackets) and mounted on a white horse—and
where should Joel get a white horse? "—" Had this real young
man made his appearance yet? "—" No; there had not been a
white horse past the place since Tuesday; so it must certainly
be to-day."

A good look-out did Harriet keep for white horses during this
fateful Saturday, and plenty did she see. It was the market-day
at B., and team after team came by with one, two, and three
white horses; cart after cart, and gig after gig, each with a
white steed: Colonel M.'s carriage, with its prancing pair—but
still no horseman. At length he appeared; but he had a great-
coat whiter than the animal he rode; another, but he was old
farmer Lewington, a married man; a third, but he was little
Lord L., a school-boy, on his Arabian pony. Besides, they all
passed the house; and as the day wore on, Harriet began, alternately, to possess her old infidelity on the score of fortune-
telling, and to let out certain apprehensions that, if the gipsy
did really possess the power of foreseeing events, and no such
horseman arrived, she might possibly be unlucky enough to die
an old maid—a fate for which, although the proper destiny of a
coquette, our village beauty seemed to entertain a very decided
aversion.

At last, just at dusk, just as Harriet, making believe to close
our casement shutters, was taking her last peep up the road,
something white appeared in the distance coming leisurely
down the hill. Was it really a horse? Was it not rather Titus
Strong's cow driving home to milking? A minute or two dissi-

L

pated that fear; it certainly was a horse, and as certainly it had a dark rider. Very slowly he descended the hill, pausing most provokingly at the end of the village, as if about to turn up the Vicarage-lane. He came on, however, and after another short stop at the Rose, rode up full to our little gate, and catching Harriet's hand as she was opening the wicket, displayed to the half-pleased, half-angry damsel the smiling triumphant face of her own Joel Brent, equipped in a new great coat, and mounted on his master's newly purchased market-nag. Oh, Joel! Joel! The gipsy! the gipsy!

THE YOUNG GIPSY

THE weather continuing fine and dry, I did not fail to revisit my gipsy encampment, which became more picturesque every day in the bright sun-gleams and lengthening shadows of a most brilliant autumn. A slight frost had strewed the green lane with the light yellow leaves of the elm—those leaves on whose yielding crispness it is so pleasant to tread, and which it is so much pleasanter to watch whirling along, " thin dancers upon air," in the fresh October breeze; whilst the reddened beech, and spotted sycamore, and the rich oaks dropping with acorns, their foliage just edging into its deep orange brown, added all the magic of colour to the original beauty of the scenery. It was undoubtedly the prettiest walk in the neighbourhood, and the one which I frequented the most.

Ever since the adventure of May, the old fortune-teller and I understood each other perfectly. She knew that I was no client, no patient, no customer (which is the fittest name for a goosecap who goes to a gipsy to ask what is to befall her?), but she also knew that I was no enemy to either her or her profession; for after all, if people choose to amuse themselves by being simpletons, it is no part of their neighbours' business to hinder them. I, on my side, liked the old gipsy exceedingly; I liked both her humour and her good-humour, and had a real respect for her cleverness. We always interchanged a smile and a nod, meet where we might. May, too, had become accustomed to the whole party. The gift of a bone from the cauldron—a bare bone—your well-fed dog likes nothing so well as such a windfall, and if stolen the relish is higher—a bare bone brought about that reconciliation. I am sorry to accuse May of accepting a bribe, but such was the fact. She now looked at the fortune-teller with great complacency, would let the boys stroke her long neck, and in her turn, would condescend to frolic with their shabby curs, who, trained to a cat-like caution and mistrust of their superiors, were as much alarmed at her advances as if a lioness had offered herself as their playfellow. There was no escaping her civility, however, so they submitted to their fate, and really seemed astonished to find themselves alive when the gambol was over. One of them, who from a tail turned over his back like a squirrel, and an amazingly snub nose, had certainly some mixture of the pug in his composition, took a great fancy to her when his fright was past; which she repaid by the sort of scornful kindness, the despotic protection, proper to her as a beauty, and a favourite, and a high-blooded greyhound—always a most proud and stately creature. The poor little mongrel used regularly to come jumping to meet her, and she as regularly turned him over and over and over, and round and round and round, like a teetotum. He liked it apparently, for he never failed to come and court the tossing whenever she went near him.

The person most interesting to me of the whole party was the young girl. She was remarkably pretty, and of the peculiar prettiness which is so frequently found amongst that singular people. Her face resembled those which Sir Joshua has often painted—rosy, round, and bright, set in such a profusion of dark curls, lighted by such eyes, and such a smile! and she smiled whenever you looked at her—she could not help it. Her figure was light and small, of low stature, and with an air of great youthfulness. In her dress she was, for a gipsy, surprisingly tidy. For the most part, that ambulatory race have a preference for rags, as forming their most appropriate wardrobe, being a part of their tools of trade, their insignia of office. I do not imagine that Harriet's friend, the fortune-teller, would have exchanged her stained tattered cloak for the thickest and brightest red cardinal that ever came out of a woollen-draper's shop. And she would have been a loser if she had. Take away that mysterious mantle, and a great part of her reputation would go too. There is much virtue in an old cloak. I question if the simplest of her clients, even Harriet herself, would have consulted her in a new one. But the young girl was tidy; not only accurately clean, and with clothes neatly and nicely adjusted to her trim little form, but with the rents darned, and the holes patched, in a way that I should be glad to see equalled by our own villagers.

Her manners were quite as ungipsy-like as her apparel, and so was her conversation; for I could not help talking to her, and was much pleased with her frankness and innocence, and the directness and simplicity of her answers. She was not the least shy; on the contrary, there was a straightforward look, a

fixing of her sweet eyes full of pleasure and reliance right upon
you, which, in the description, might seem almost too assured,
but which, in reality, no more resembled vulgar assurance than
did the kindred artlessness of Shakspeare's Miranda. It seems
strange to liken a gipsy girl to that loveliest creation of genius;
but I never saw that innocent gaze without being sure that just
with such a look of pleased attention, of affectionate curiosity,
did the island princess listen to Ferdinand.

All that she knew of her little story she told without scruple,
in a young liquid voice, and with a little curtsy between every
answer, that became her extremely. " Her name," she said,
" was Fanny. She had no father or mother; they were dead;
and she and her brothers lived with her grandmother. They
lived always out of doors, sometimes in one place—sometimes
in another; but she should like always to live under that oak-
tree, it was so pleasant. Her grandmother was very good to
them all, only rather particular. She loved her very much;
and she loved Dick (her eldest brother), though he was a sad
unlucky boy, to be sure. She was afraid he would come to
some bad end."

And, indeed, Dick at that moment seemed in imminent
danger of verifying his sister's prediction. He had been trying
for a gleaning of nuts amongst the tall hazels on the top of a
bank, which, flanked by a deep ditch, separated the coppice
from the green. We had heard him for the last five minutes
smashing and crashing away at a prodigious rate, swinging himself from stalk to stalk, and tugging and climbing like a sailor
or a monkey; and now, at the very instant of Fanny's uttering
this prophecy, having missed a particularly venturesome grasp,
he was impelled forward by the rebound of the branches, and
fell into the ditch with a tremendous report, bringing half the
nuttery after him, and giving us all a notion that he had broken
his neck. His time, however, was not yet come: he was on his
feet again in half a minute and in another half minute we again
heard him rustling among the hazel boughs; and Fanny and
I went on with our talk, which the fright and scolding, conse-
quent on this accident, had interrupted. My readers are of
course aware, that when any one meets with a fall, the approved
medicament of the most affectionate relative is a good dose of
scolding.

" She liked Dick," she continued, " in spite of his unluckiness

—he was so quick and good-humoured; but the person she loved most was her youngest brother, Willy. Willy was the best boy in the world, he would do anything she told him " (indeed the poor child was in the very act of picking up acorns under her inspection, to sell, as I afterwards found, in the village), " and never got into mischief, or told a lie in his life; she had had the care of him ever since he was born, and she wished she could get him a place." By this time the little boy had crept towards us, and still collecting the acorns in his small brown hands, had turned up his keen intelligent face, and was listening with great interest to our conversation. " A place! " said I, much surprised. " Yes," replied she firmly, " a place. 'Twould be a fine thing for my poor Willy to have a house over him in the cold winter nights." And with a grave tenderness, that might have beseemed a young mother, she stooped her head over the boy and kissed him. " But *you* sleep out of doors in the cold winter nights, Fanny?"—" Me! oh, I don't mind it, and sometimes we creep into a barn. But poor Willy! If I could but get Willy a place, my lady! "

This " my lady," the first gipsy word that Fanny had uttered, lost all that it would have had of unpleasing in the generosity and affectionateness of the motive. I could not help promising to recommend her Willy, although I could not hold out any very strong hopes of success, and we parted, Fanny following me, with thanks upon thanks, almost to the end of the lane.

Two days after I again saw my pretty gipsy; she was standing by the side of our gate, too modest even to enter the court, waiting for my coming out to speak to me. I brought her into the hall, and was almost equally delighted to see her, and to hear her news; for although I had most faithfully performed my promise, by mentioning master Willy to everybody likely to want a servant of his qualifications, I had seen enough in the course of my canvass to convince me that a gipsy boy of eight years old would be a difficult protégé to provide for.

Fanny's errand relieved my perplexity. She came to tell me that Willy had gotten a place—" That Thomas Lamb, my lord's head gamekeeper, had hired him to tend his horse and his cow, and serve the pigs, and feed the dogs, and dig the garden, and clean the shoes and knives, and run on errands—in short, to be a man of all work. Willy was gone that very morning. He had cried to part with her, and she had almost cried herself, she should miss him so; he was like her own child. But then it was such a great place; and Thomas Lamb seemed such a kind master—talked of new clothing him, and meant him to wear shoes and stockings, and was very kind indeed. But poor Willy had cried sadly at leaving her "—and the sweet matronly elder sister fairly cried too.

I comforted her all I could, first by praises of Thomas Lamb, who happened to be of my acquaintance, and was indeed the very master whom, had I had the choice, I would have selected for Willy; and secondly, by the gift of some unconsidered trifles, which one should have been ashamed to offer to any one who had ever had a house over her head, but which the pretty gipsy girl received with transport, especially some working materials of the commonest sort. Poor Fanny had never known the luxury of a thimble before; it was as new to her finger as shoes and stockings were likely to be to Willy's feet. She forgot her sorrows, and tripped home to her oak-tree, the happiest of the happy.

Thomas Lamb, Willy's new master, was, as I have said, of my acquaintance. He was a remarkably fine young man, and as well-mannered as those of his calling usually are. Generally speaking there are no persons, excepting real gentlemen, so gentlemanly as gamekeepers. They keep good company. The beautiful and graceful creatures whom they at once preserve and pursue, and the equally noble and generous animals whom they train, are their principal associates; and even by their masters they are regarded rather as companions than as servants. They attend them in their sports more as guides and leaders than as followers, pursuing a common recreation with equal enjoyment, and often with superior skill. Gamekeepers are almost always well behaved, and Thomas Lamb was eminently so. He had quite the look of a man of fashion; the person, the carriage, the air. His figure was tall and striking; his features delicately carved, with a paleness of complexion, and a slight appearance of ill-health that added to their elegance. In short, he was exactly what the ladies would have called interesting in a gentleman; and the gentleness of his voice and manner, and the constant propriety of his deportment, tended to confirm the impression.

Luckily for him, however, this delicacy and refinement lay chiefly on the surface. His constitution, habits, and temper, were much better fitted to his situation, much hardier and heartier, than they appeared to be. He was still a bachelor, and lived by himself in a cottage, almost as lonely as if it had been placed in a desert island. It stood in the centre of his preserves, in the midst of a wilderness of coppice and woodland, accessible only by a narrow winding path, and at least a mile from the nearest habitation. When you had threaded the labyrinth, and were fairly arrived in Thomas's dominion, it was a pretty territory. A low thatched cottage, very irregularly built, with a porch before the door, and a vine half covering the casements; a garden a good deal neglected (Thomas Lamb's four-footed subjects, the hares, took care to eat up all his flowers: hares are animals of taste, and are particularly fond of pinks and carnations, the rogues!), an orchard and a meadow completed the demesne. There was also a commodious dog-kennel, and a stable, of which the outside was completely covered with the trophies of Thomas's industry — kites, jackdaws, magpies, hawks, crows, and owls, nailed by the wings, *displayed*, as they say in heraldry, against the wall, with polecats, weazels, stoats, and hedgehogs figuring at their side, a perfect menagerie of dead game-killers.[1]

But the prettiest part of this woodland cottage was the real living game that flitted about it, as tame as barn-door fowls; partridges flocking to be fed, as if there were not a dog, or a gun, or a man in the world; pheasants, glorious creatures! coming at a call; hares almost as fearless as Cowper's, that would stand and let you look at them: would let you approach quite near, before they raised one quivering ear and darted off; and that even then, when the instinct of timidity was aroused, would turn at a safe distance to look again. Poor, pretty things! What a pity it seemed to kill them!

Such was to be Willy's future habitation. The day after he entered upon his place, I had an opportunity of offering my double congratulations, to the master on his new servant, to the servant on his new master. Whilst taking my usual walk, I found Thomas Lamb, Dick, Willy, and Fanny, about half-way

---

[1] Foxes, the destruction of which is so great an object in a pheasant preserve, never are displayed, especially if there be a pack of hounds in the neighbourhood. That odious part of a gamekeeper's occupation is as quietly and unostentatiously performed as any operation of gunnery can be. Lords of manors will even affect to preserve foxes—Heaven forgive them! just as an unpopular ministry is sure to talk of protecting the liberty of the subject.

up the lane, engaged in the animating sport of unearthing a weazel, which one of the gipsy dogs followed into a hole by the ditch-side. The boys showed great sportsmanship on this occasion: and so did their poor curs, who, with their whole bodies inserted into the different branches of the burrow, and nothing visible but their tails (the one, the long puggish brush, of which I have already made mention, the other a terrier-like stump that maintained an incessant wag), continued to dig and scratch, throwing out showers of earth, and whining with impatience and eagerness. Every now and then, when quite gasping and exhausted, they came out for a moment's air; whilst the boys took their turn, poking with a long stick, or loosening the ground with their hands, and Thomas stood by, superintending and encouraging both dog and boy, and occasionally cutting a root or a bramble that impeded their progress. Fanny, also, entered into the pursuit with great interest, dropping here and there a word of advice, as nobody can help doing when they see others in perplexity. In spite of all these aids, the mining operation proceeded so slowly, that the experienced keeper sent off his new attendant for a spade to dig out the vermin, and I pursued my walk.

After this encounter, it so happened that I never went near the gipsy tent without meeting Thomas Lamb—sometimes on foot, sometimes on his pony; now with a gun, and now without; but always loitering near the oak-tree, and always, as it seemed, reluctant to be seen. It was very unlike Thomas's usual manner to seem ashamed of being caught in any place, or in any company; but so it was. Did he go to the ancient sibyl to get his fortune told? or was Fanny the attraction? A very short time solved the query.

One night, towards the end of the month, the keeper presented himself at our house on justice business. He wanted a summons for some poachers who had been committing depredations in the preserve. Thomas was a great favourite; and was, of course, immediately admitted, his examination taken, and his request complied with. " But how," said the magistrate, looking up from the summons which he was signing, " how can you expect, Thomas, to keep your pheasants, when that gipsy boy with his finders has pitched his tent just in the midst of your best coppices, killing more game than half the poachers in the country? "—" Why, as to the gipsy, sir," replied Thomas,

" Fanny is as good a girl—" " I was not talking of Fanny,"
interrupted the man of warrants, smiling—" as good a girl,"
pursued Thomas—" A very pretty girl! " ejaculated his worship—" as good a girl," resumed Thomas, " as ever trod the
earth! "—" A sweet pretty creature, certainly," was again the
provoking reply. " Ah, sir, if you could but hear how her little
brother talks of her! "—" Why, Thomas, this gipsy has made
an impression."—" Ah, sir! she is such a good girl! "—and the
next day they were married.

It was a measure to set every tongue in the village a wagging;
for Thomas, besides his personal good gifts, was well-to-do in
the world—my lord's head keeper, and prime favourite. He
might have pretended to any farmer's daughter in the parish:
everybody cried out against the match. It was rather a bold
measure, certainly; but I think it will end well. They are,
beyond a doubt, the handsomest couple in these parts; and as
the fortune-teller and her eldest grandson have had the good
sense to decamp, and Fanny, besides being the most grateful
and affectionate creature on earth, turns out clever and docile,
and comports herself just as if she had lived in a house all her
days, there are some hopes that in process of time her sin of
gipsyism may be forgiven, and Mrs Lamb be considered as visit-
able, at least by her next neighbours, the wives of the shoemaker
and the parish clerk. At present, I am sorry to say that those
worthy persons have sent both Thomas and her to Coventry—a
misfortune which they endure with singular resignation.

MAY the 3rd.—Cold bright weather. All within doors, sunny and chilly; all without, windy and dusty. It is quite tantalizing to see that brilliant sun careering through so beautiful a sky, and to feel little more warmth from his presence than one does from that of his fair but cold sister, the moon. Even the sky, beautiful as it is, has the look of that one sometimes sees in a very bright moonlight night—deeply, intensely blue, with white fleecy clouds driven vigorously along by a strong breeze—now veiling and now exposing the dazzling luminary around whom they sail. A beautiful sky! and, in spite of its coldness, a beautiful world! The effect of this backward spring has been to arrest the early flowers, to which heat is the great enemy; whilst the leaves and the later flowers have, nevertheless, ventured to peep out slowly and cautiously in sunny places—exhibiting, in the copses and hedgerows, a pleasant mixture of March and May. And we, poor chilly mortals, must follow, as nearly as we can, the wise example of the May-blossoms, by avoiding bleak paths and open commons, and creeping up the sheltered road to the vicarage—the pleasant sheltered road, where the western sun steals in between two rows of bright-green elms, and the east wind is fenced off by the range of woody hills which rise abruptly before us, forming so striking a boundary to the picture.

How pretty this lane is, with its tall elms, just dressed in their young leaves, bordering the sunny path, or sweeping in a semicircle behind the clear pools, and the white cottages that are scattered along the way. You shall seldom see a cottage hereabout without an accompanying pond, all alive with geese and ducks, at the end of the little garden. Ah! here is Dame Simmons making a most original use of her piece of water, standing on the bank that divides it from her garden, and most ingeniously watering her onion-bed with a new mop—now a dip, and now a twirl! Really, I give her credit for the invention. It is as good an imitation of a shower as one should wish to see on a summer day. A squirt is nothing to it!

And here is another break to the tall line of elms—the gate

that leads into Farmer Thorpe's great enclosures. Eight, ten, fourteen people in this large field, wheat-hoeing. The couple nearest the gate, who keep aloof from all the rest, and are hoeing this furrow so completely in concert, step by step, and stroke for stroke, are Jem Tanner and Mabel Green. There is not a handsomer pair in the field or in the village. Jem, with his bright complexion, his curling hair, his clear blue eye, and his trim figure—set off to great advantage by his short jacket and trousers and new straw hat; Mabel, with her little stuff gown, and her white handkerchief and apron—defining so exactly her light and flexible shape—and her black eyes flashing from under a deep bonnet lined with pink, whose reflection gives to her bright dark countenance and dimpled cheeks a glow innocently artificial, which was the only charm that they wanted.

Jem and Mabel are, beyond all doubt, the handsomest couple in the field, and I am much mistaken if each have not a vivid sense of the charms of the other. Their mutual admiration was clear enough in their work; but it speaks still more plainly in their idleness. Not a stroke have they done for these five minutes; Jem, propped on his hoe, and leaning across the furrow, whispering soft nonsense; Mabel, blushing and smiling—now making believe to turn away—now listening, and looking up with a sweeter smile than ever, and a blush that makes her bonnet-lining pale. Ah, Mabel! Mabel! Now they are going to work again—no!—after three or four strokes the hoes have somehow become entangled, and, without either advancing a step nearer the other, they are playing with these rustic implements as pretty a game at romps—showing off as nice a piece of rural flirtation—as ever was exhibited since wheat was hoed.

Ah, Mabel! Mabel! beware of Farmer Thorpe! He'll see, at a glance, that little will his corn profit by such labours. Beware, too, Jem Tanner!—for Mabel is, in some sort, an heiress; being the real niece and adopted daughter of our little lame clerk, who, although he looks such a tattered ragamuffin, that the very grave-diggers are ashamed of him, is well to pass in the world—keeps a scrub pony—indeed he can hardly walk up the aisle—hath a share in the County fire-office—and money in the funds. Mabel will be an heiress, despite the tatterdemalion costume of her honoured uncle, which I think he wears out of coquetry, that the remarks which might otherwise fall on his miserable person—full as misshapen as that of any Hunchback recorded in the Arabian Tales—may find a less offensive vent on his raiment. Certain such a figure hath seldom been beheld out of church or in. Yet will Mabel, nevertheless, be a fortune; and, therefore, she must intermarry with another fortune, according to the rule made and provided in such cases; and the little clerk hath already looked her out a spouse, about his own standing—a widower in the next parish, with four children and a squint. Poor Jem Tanner! Nothing will that smart person or that pleasant speech avail with the little clerk; never will he officiate at your marriage to his niece; " amen " would " stick in his throat." Poor things! in what a happy oblivion of the world and its cares, Farmer Thorpe and the wheat-hoeing, the squinting shopkeeper and the little clerk, are they laughing and talking at this moment! Poor things! poor things!

Well, I must pursue my walk. How beautiful a mixture of flowers and leaves is in the high bank under this north hedge— quite an illustration of the blended seasons of which I spoke. An old irregular hedgerow is always beautiful, especially in the spring-time, when the grass, and mosses, and flowering weeds mingle best with the bushes and creeping plants that overhang them. But this bank is, most especially, various and lovely. Shall we try to analyse it ? First, the clinging white-veined ivy, which crawls up the slope in every direction, the master-piece of that rich mosaic; then the brown leaves and the lilac blossoms of its fragrant namesake, the ground-ivy, which grows here so profusely; then the late-lingering primrose; then the delicate wood-sorrel; then the regular pink stars of the cranesbill, with its beautiful leaves; then the golden oxslip and the cowslip, " cinque-spotted "; then the blue pansy, and the enamelled wild hyacinth; then the bright foliage of the brier-rose, which comes trailing its green wreaths amongst the flowers; then the bramble and the woodbine, creeping round the foot of a pollard oak, with its brown folded leaves; then a verdant mass—the blackthorn, with its lingering blossoms—the hawthorn, with its swelling buds—the bushy maple—the long stems of the hazel— and between them, hanging like a golden plume over the bank, a splendid tuft of the blossomed broom; then, towering high above all, the tall and leafy elms. And this is but a faint picture of this hedge, on the meadowy side of which sheep are bleating, and where, every here and there, a young lamb is thrusting its pretty head between the trees.

Who is this approaching? Farmer Thorpe? Yes, of a certainty, it is that substantial yeoman, sallying forth from his substantial farm-house, which peeps out from between two huge walnut-trees on the other side of the road, with intent to survey his labourers in the wheat-field. Farmer Thorpe is a stout, square, sturdy personage of fifty, or thereabout, with a hard weather-beaten countenance, of that peculiar vermilion, all over alike, into which the action of the sun and wind sometimes tans a fair complexion; sharp shrewd features, and a keen grey eye. He looks completely like a man who will neither cheat nor be cheated: and such is his character—an upright, downright English yeoman—just always, and kind in a rough way—but given to fits of anger, and filled with an abhorrence of pilfering, and idleness, and trickery of all sorts, that makes him strict as a master, and somewhat stern at workhouse and vestry. I doubt if he will greatly relish the mode in which Jem and Mabel are administering the hoe in his wheat-drills. He will not reach the gate yet; for his usual steady active pace is turned, by a recent accident, into an unequal, impatient halt—as if he were alike angry with his lameness and the cause. I must speak to him as he passes—not merely as a due courtesy to a good neighbour, but to give the delinquents in the field notice to resume their hoeing; but not a word of the limp—that is a sore subject.

" A fine day, Mr Thorpe! "

" We want rain, ma'am! "

And on, with great civility, but without pausing a moment, he is gone. He'll certainly catch Mabel and her lover philandering over his wheat-furrows. Well, that may take its chance! —they have his lameness in their favour—only that the cause of that lameness has made the worthy farmer unusually cross. I think I must confide the story to my readers.

Gipsies and beggars do not in general much inhabit our neighbourhood; but, about half a mile off, there is a den so convenient for strollers and vagabonds that it sometimes tempts the rogues to a few days' sojourn. It is, in truth, nothing more than a deserted brick-kiln, by the side of a lonely lane. But there is something so snug and comfortable in the old building (always keeping in view gipsy notions of comfort); the blackened walls are so backed by the steep hill on whose side they are built—so fenced from the bleak north-east, and letting in so gaily the pleasant western sun; and the wide rugged impassable lane (used only as a road to the kiln, and with that abandoned) is at once so solitary and deserted, and so close to the inhabited and populous world, that it seems made for a tribe whose prime requisites in a habitation are shelter, privacy, and a vicinity to farm-yards.

Accordingly, about a month ago, a pretty strong encampment, evidently gipsies, took up their abode in the kiln. The party consisted of two or three tall, lean, sinister-looking men, who went about the country mending pots and kettles, and driving a small trade in old iron; one or two children, unnaturally quiet, the spies of the crew; an old woman, who sold matches and told fortunes; a young woman, with an infant strapped to her back, who begged; several hungry-looking dogs, and three ragged donkeys. The arrival of these vagabonds spread a general consternation through the village. Gamekeepers and housewives were in equal dismay. Snares were found in the preserves—poultry vanished from the farm-yards—a lamb was lost from the lea—and a damask table-cloth, belonging to the worshipful the Mayor of W——, was abstracted from the drying-ground of Rachel Strong, the most celebrated laundress in these parts, to whom it had been sent for the benefit of country washing. No end to the pilfering, and the stories of pilfering! The inhabitants of the kiln were not only thieves in themselves, but the cause of thievery in others. " The gipsies! " was the answer general to every inquiry for things missing.

Farmer Thorpe—whose dwelling, with its variety of outbuildings—barns, ricks, and stables—is only separated by a meadow and a small coppice from the lane that leads to the gipsy retreat—was particularly annoyed by this visitation. Two couple of full-grown ducks, and a whole brood of early chickens, disappeared in one night; and Mrs Thorpe fretted over the loss, and the farmer was indignant at the roguery. He set traps, let loose mastiffs, and put in action all the resources of village police—but in vain. Every night property went; and the culprits, however strongly suspected, still continued unamenable to the law.

At last, one morning, the great Chanticleer of the farm-yard— a cock of a million, with an unrivalled crow—a matchless strut, and plumage all gold and green, and orange and purple—

gorgeous as a peacock, and fierce as a he-turkey—Chanticleer,
the pride and glory of the yard, was missing! and Mrs Thorpe's
lamentations and her husband's anger redoubled. Vowing
vengeance against the gipsies, he went to the door to survey a
young blood mare of his own breeding; and as he stood at the
gate—now bemoaning Chanticleer—now cursing the gipsies—
now admiring the bay filly—his neighbour, Dame Simmons—
the identical lady of the mop, who occasionally chared at the
house—came to give him the comfortable information that she
had certainly heard Chanticleer—she was quite ready to swear
to Chanticleer's voice—crowing in the brick-kiln. No time, she
added, should be lost, if Farmer Thorpe wished to rescue that
illustrious cock, and to punish the culprits—since the gipsies,
when she passed the place, were preparing to decamp.

No time *was* lost. In one moment Farmer Thorpe was on
the bay filly's unsaddled back, with the halter for a bridle;
and, in the next, they were on full gallop towards the kiln.
But, alas! alas! " the more haste the worse speed," says the
wisdom of nations. Just as they arrived at the spot from which
the procession—gipsies, dogs, and donkeys—and Chanticleer in
a sack, shrieking most vigorously—were proceeding on their
travels, the young blood mare—whether startled at the unusual
cortège, or the rough ways, or the hideous noise of her old friend,
the cock—suddenly reared and threw her master, who lay in
all the agony of a sprained ankle, unable to rise from the ground;
whilst the whole tribe, with poor Chanticleer their prisoner,
marched triumphantly past him, utterly regardless of his threats
and imprecations. In this plight was the unlucky farmer discovered, about half an hour afterwards, by his wife, the constable, and a party of his own labourers, who came to give him
assistance in securing the culprits; of whom, notwithstanding
an instant and active search through the neighbourhood, nothing has yet transpired. We shall hardly see them again in
these parts, and have almost done talking of them. The village
is returned to its old state of order and honesty; the Mayor of
W—— has replaced his table-cloth, and Mrs Thorpe her cock;
and the poor farmer's lame ankle is all that remains to give
token of the gipsies.

Here we are at the turning which, edging round by the
coppice, branches off to their some-time den: the other bend
to the right leads up a gentle ascent to the vicarage, and that

is our way. How fine a view of the little parsonage we have
from hence, between those arching elms, which enclose it like
a picture in a frame! and how pretty a picture it forms, with
its three pointed roofs, its snug porch, and its casement windows
glittering from amid the China-roses! What a nest of peace and
comfort! Farther on, almost at the summit of the hill, stands
the old church with its massy tower—a row of superb lime-trees
running along one side of the church-yard, and a cluster of dark
yews shading the other. Few country churches have so much
to boast in architectural beauty, or in grandeur of situation.

We lose sight of it as we mount the hill, the lane narrowing
and winding between deep banks, surmounted by high hedges,
excluding all prospects till we reach the front of the vicarage,
and catch across the gate of the opposite field a burst of country
the most extensive and the most beautiful—field and village,
mansion and cot, town and river, all smiling under the sparkling sun of May, and united and harmonized by the profusion
of hedgerow timber in its freshest verdure, giving a rich woodland character to the scene, till it is terminated in the distance
by the blue line of the Hampshire hills almost melting into the
horizon. Such is the view from the vicarage. But it is too sunny
and too windy to stand about out of doors, and time to finish
our ramble. Down the hill, and round the corner, and past
Farmer Thorpe's house, and one glance at the wheat-hoers, and
then we will go home.

Ah! it is just as I feared. Jem and Mabel have been parted:
they are now at opposite sides of the field—he looking very
angry, working rapidly and violently, and doing more harm
than good—she looking tolerably sulky, and just moving her
hoe, but evidently doing nothing at all. Farmer Thorpe, on
his part, is standing in the middle of the field, observing, but
pretending not to observe, the little humours of the separated
lovers. There is a lurking smile about the corners of his mouth
that bespeaks him more amused than angry. He is a kind person
after all, and will certainly make no mischief. I should not even
wonder if he espoused Jem Tanner's cause; and, for certain, if
any one can prevail on the little clerk to give up his squinting
favourite in favour of true love, Farmer Thorpe is the man.

M

THE pride of my heart and the delight of my eyes is my garden. Our house, which is in dimensions very much like a bird-cage, and might, with almost equal convenience, be laid on a shelf, or hung up in a tree, would be utterly unbearable in warm weather, were it not that we have a retreat out of doors— and a very pleasant retreat it is. To make my readers comprehend it, I must describe our whole territories.

Fancy a small plot of ground, with a pretty low irregular cottage at one end; a large granary, divided from the dwelling by a little court running along one side; and a long thatched shed, open towards the garden, and supported by wooden pillars, on the other. The bottom is bounded, half by an old wall, and half by an old paling, over which we see a pretty distance of woody hills. The house, granary, wall, and paling, are covered with vines, cherry-trees, roses, honeysuckles, and jessamines, with great clusters of tall hollyhocks running up between them; a large elder overhanging the little gate, and a magnificent bay-tree, such a tree as shall scarcely be matched in these parts, breaking with its beautiful conical form the horizontal lines of the buildings. This is my garden; and the long pillared shed, the sort of rustic arcade, which runs along one side, parted from the flower-beds by a row of rich geraniums, is our out-of-door drawing-room.

I know nothing so pleasant as to sit there on a summer afternoon, with the western sun flickering through the great elder-tree, and lighting up our gay parterres, where flowers and flowering shrubs are set as thick as grass in a field, a wilderness of blossom, interwoven, intertwined, wreathy, garlandy, profuse beyond all profusion, where we may guess that there is such a thing as mould, but never see it. I know nothing so pleasant as to sit in the shade of that dark bower, with the eye resting on that bright piece of colour, lighted so gloriously by the evening sun, now catching a glimpse of the little birds as they fly rapidly in and out of their nests—for there are always two or three birds' nests in the thick tapestry of cherry-trees, honeysuckles, and China-roses, which covers our walls—now tracing the gay gambols of the common butterflies as they sport around the dahlias; now watching that rarer moth, which the country people, fertile in pretty names, call the bee-bird;[1] that bird-like insect which flutters in the hottest days over the sweetest flowers, inserting its long proboscis into the small tube of the jessamine, and hovering over the scarlet blossoms of the geranium, whose bright colour seems reflected on its own feathery breast: that insect which seems so thoroughly a creature of the air, never at rest; always, even when feeding, self-poised, and self-supported, and whose wings, in their cease-less motion, have a sound so deep, so full, so lulling, so musical. Nothing so pleasant as to sit amid that mixture of the flower and the leaf, watching the bee-bird! Nothing so pretty to look at as my garden! It is quite a picture; only unluckily it resembles a picture in more qualities than one—it is fit for nothing but to look at. One might as well think of walking in a bit of framed canvas. There are walks to be sure—tiny paths of smooth gravel, by courtesy called such—but they are so overhung by roses and lilies, and such gay encroachers—so over-run by con-volvulus, and heart's-ease, and mignonette, and other sweet stragglers, that, except to edge through them occasionally, for the purposes of planting, or weeding, or watering, there might as well be no paths at all. Nobody thinks of walking in my garden. Even May glides along with a delicate and trackless step, like a swan through the water; and we, its two-footed denizens, are fain to treat it as if it were really a saloon, and go out for a walk towards sunset, just as if we had not been sitting in the open air all day.

What a contrast from the quiet garden to the lively street! Saturday night is always a time of stir and bustle in our village, and this is Whitsun-Eve, the pleasantest Saturday of all the year, when London journeymen and servant lads and lasses snatch a short holiday, to visit their families. A short and precious holi-day, the happiest and liveliest of any; for even the gambols and merry-makings of Christmas offer but a poor enjoyment com-pared with the rural diversions, the Mayings, revels, and cricket matches of Whitsuntide.

We ourselves are to have a cricket match on Monday, not played by the men, who, since a certain misadventure with the Beech-hillers, are, I am sorry to say, rather chap-fallen, but by

[1] *Sphinx ligustri*, privet hawk-moth.

the boys, who, zealous for the honour of their parish, and headed by their bold leader, Ben Kirby, marched in a body to our antagonists' ground the Sunday after our melancholy defeat, challenged the boys of that proud hamlet, and beat them out and out on the spot. Never was a more signal victory. Our boys enjoyed this triumph with so little moderation that it had like to have produced a very tragical catastrophe. The captain of the Beech-hill youngsters, a capital bowler, by name Amos Stone, enraged past all bearing by the crowing of his adversaries, flung the ball at Ben Kirby with so true an aim, that if that sagacious leader had not warily ducked his head when he saw it coming, there would probably have been a coroner's inquest on the case, and Amos Stone would have been tried for manslaughter. He let fly with such vengeance that the cricket-ball was found embedded in a bank of clay five hundred yards off, as if it had been a cannon shot. Tom Coper and Farmer Thackum, the umpires, both say that they never saw so tremendous a ball. If Amos Stone live to be a man (I mean to say, if he be not hanged first) he'll be a pretty player. He is coming here on Monday with his party to play the return match, the umpires having respectively engaged, Farmer Thackum that Amos shall keep the peace, Tom Coper that Ben shall give no unnecessary or wanton provocation—a nicely worded and lawyer-like clause, and one that proves that Tom Coper hath his doubts of the young gentleman's discretion; and, of a truth, so have I. I would not be Ben Kirby's surety, cautiously as the security is worded—no! not for a white double dahlia, the present object of my ambition.

This village of ours is swarming to-night like a hive of bees, and all the church bells round are pouring out their merriest peals, as if to call them together. I must try to give some notion of the various figures.

First there is a group suited to Teniers, a cluster of out-of-door customers of the Rose, old benchers of the inn, who sit round a table smoking and drinking in high solemnity to the sound of Timothy's fiddle. Next, a mass of eager boys, the combatants of Monday, who are surrounding the shoemaker's shop, where an invisible hole in their ball is mending by Master Keep himself, under the joint superintendence of Ben Kirby and Tom Coper. Ben showing much verbal respect and outward deference for his umpire's judgment and experience, but managing to get the ball done his own way after all; whilst outside the shop, the rest of the eleven, the less trusted commons, are shouting and bawling round Joel Brent, who is twisting the waxed twine round the handles of the bats—the poor bats, which please nobody, which the taller youths are despising as too little and too light, and the smaller are abusing as too heavy and too large. Happy critics! winning their match can hardly be a greater delight—even if to win it they be doomed! Farther down the street is the pretty black-eyed girl, Sally Wheeler, come home for a day's holiday from B., escorted by a tall footman in a dashing livery, whom she is trying to curtsy off before her deaf grandmother sees him. I wonder whether she will succeed!

Ascending the hill are two couples of a different description. Daniel Tubb and his fair Valentine, walking boldly along like licensed lovers; they have been asked twice in church, and are to be married on Tuesday; and closely following that happy pair, near each other, but not together, come Jem Tanner and Mabel Green, the poor culprits of the wheat-hoeing. Ah! the little clerk hath not relented! The course of true love doth not yet run smooth in that quarter. Jem dodges along, whistling "cherry-ripe," pretending to walk by himself, and to be thinking of nobody; but every now and then he pauses in his negligent saunter, and turns round outright to steal a glance at Mabel, who, on her part, is making believe to walk with poor Olive Hathaway, the lame mantua-maker, and even affecting to talk and to listen to that gentle, humble creature, as she points to the wild flowers on the common, and the lambs and children disporting amongst the gorse, but whose thoughts and eyes are evidently fixed on Jem Tanner, as she meets his backward glance with a blushing smile, and half springs forward to meet him; whilst Olive has broken off the conversation as soon as she perceived the preoccupation of her companion, and begun humming, perhaps unconsciously, two or three lines of Burns, whose "Whistle and I'll come to thee, my love" and "Gi'e me a glance of thy bonnie black ee" were never better exemplified than in the couple before her. Really it is curious to watch them, and to see how gradually the attraction of this tantalizing vicinity becomes irresistible, and the rustic lover rushes to his pretty mistress like the needle to the magnet. On they go, trusting to the deepening twilight, to the little clerk's absence,

to the good humour of the happy lads and lasses, who are passing and repassing on all sides—or rather, perhaps, in a happy
oblivion of the cross uncle, the kind villagers, the squinting
lover, and the whole world. On they trip, linked arm in arm,
he trying to catch a glimpse of her glowing face under her
bonnet, and she hanging down her head and avoiding his gaze
with a mixture of modesty and coquetry which well becomes
the rural beauty. On they go, with a reality and intensity of
affection which must overcome all obstacles; and poor Olive
follows with an evident sympathy in their happiness, which
makes her almost as enviable as they; and we pursue our walk
amidst the moonshine and the nightingales, with Jacob Frost's
cart looming in the distance, and the merry sounds of Whitsuntide, the shout, the laugh, and the song, echoing all around us
like " noises of the air."

OUR MAYING

AS party produces party, and festival brings forth festival, in higher life, so one scene of rural festivity is pretty sure to be followed by another. The boys' cricket match at Whitsuntide, which was won most triumphantly by our parish, and luckily passed off without giving cause for a coroner's inquest, or indeed without injury of any sort, except the demolition of Amos Stone's new straw hat, the crown of which (Amos's head being fortunately at a distance) was fairly struck out by the cricket-ball; this match produced one between our eleven and the players of the neighbouring hamlet of Whitley; and being patronized by the young lord of the manor and several of the gentry round, and followed by jumping in sacks, riding donkey races, grinning through horse-collars, and other diversions more renowned for their antiquity than their elegance, gave such general satisfaction, that it was resolved to hold a Maying in full form in Whitley-wood.

Now this wood of ours happens to be a common of twenty acres, with three trees on it, and the Maying was fixed to be held between hay-time and harvest; but " what's in a name ? " Whitley-wood is a beautiful piece of green sward, surrounded on three sides by fields, and farm-houses, and cottages, and woody uplands, and on the other by a fine park; and the May-house was erected and the May-games held in the beginning of July, the very season of leaves and roses, when the days are at the longest, and the weather at the finest, and the whole world is longing to get out of doors. Moreover, the whole festival was aided, not impeded, by the gentlemen amateurs, headed by that very genial person, our young lord of the manor; whilst the business part of the affair was confided to the well-known diligence, zeal, activity, and intelligence of that most popular of village landlords, mine host of the Rose. How could a Maying fail under such auspices ? Everybody expected more sunshine and more fun, more flowers and more laughing, than ever was known at a rustic merry-making—and really, considering the manner in which expectation had been raised, the quantity of disappointment has been astonishingly small.

Landlord Sims, the master of the revels, and our very good neighbour, is a portly, bustling man of five-and-forty, or thereabout, with a hale, jovial visage, a merry eye, a pleasant smile, and a general air of good-fellowship. This last qualification, whilst it serves greatly to recommend his ale, is apt to mislead superficial observers, who generally account him a sort of a slenderer Boniface, and imagine that, like that renowned hero of the spiggot, Master Sims eats, drinks, and sleeps on his own anno domini. They were never more mistaken in their lives; no soberer man than Master Sims within twenty miles! Except for the good of the house, he no more thinks of drinking beer than a grocer of eating figs. To be sure when the jug lags he will take a hearty pull, just by way of example, and to set the good ale a going. But, in general, he trusts to subtler and more delicate modes of quickening its circulation. A good song, a good story, a merry jest, a hearty laugh, and a most winning habit of assentation; these are his implements. There is not a better companion, or a more judicious listener, in the county. His pliability is astonishing. He shall say yes to twenty different opinions on the same subject, within the hour; and so honest and cordial does his agreement seem, that no one of his customers, whether drunk or sober, ever dreams of doubting his sincerity. The hottest conflict of politics never puzzles him: Whig or Tory, he is both, or either—" the happy Mercutio, that curses both houses." Add to this gift of conformity a cheerful, easy temper, an alacrity of attention, a zealous desire to please, which gives to his duties, as a landlord, all the grace of hospitality, and a perpetual civility and kindness, even when he has nothing to gain by them; and no one can wonder at Master Sims's popularity.

After his good wife's death, this popularity began to extend itself in a remarkable manner amongst the females of the neighbourhood; smitten with his portly person, his smooth, oily manner, and a certain soft, earnest, whispering voice, which he generally assumes when addressing one of the fairer sex, and which seems to make his very " how d'ye do " confidential and complimentary. Moreover, it was thought that the good landlord was well-to-do in the world, and though Betsy and Letty were good little girls, quick, civil, and active, yet, poor things, what could such young girls know of a house like the Rose? All would go to rack and ruin without the eye of a mistress!

Master Sims must look out for a wife. So thought the whole female world, and, apparently, Master Sims began to think so himself.

The first fair one to whom his attention was directed, was a rosy, pretty widow, a pastrycook of the next town, who arrived in our village on a visit to her cousin, the baker, for the purpose of giving confectionery lessons to his wife. Nothing was ever so hot as that courtship. During the week that the lady of pie-crust stayed, her lover almost lived in the oven. One would have thought that he was learning to make the cream tarts without pepper, by which Bedreddin Hassan regained his state and his princess. It would be a most suitable match, as all the parish agreed; the widow, for as pretty as she was (and one shan't often see a pleasanter open countenance, or a sweeter smile), being within ten years as old as her suitor, and having had two husbands already. A most proper and suitable match, said everybody; and when our landlord carried her back to B. in his new-painted green cart, all the village agreed that they were gone to be married, and the ringers were just setting up a peal, when Master Sims returned alone, single, crest-fallen, dejected; the bells stopped of themselves, and we heard no more of the pretty pastrycook. For three months after that rebuff, mine host, albeit not addicted to aversions, testified an equal dislike to women and tartlets, widows and plum-cake. Even poor Alice Taylor, whose travelling basket of lollypops and ginger-bread he had whilom patronized, was forbidden the house; and not a bun or a biscuit could be had at the Rose for love or money.

The fit, however, wore off in time; and he began again to follow the advice of his neighbours, and to look out for a wife, up street and down; whilst at each extremity a fair object presented herself, from neither of whom had he the slightest reason to dread a repetition of the repulse which he had experienced from the blooming widow. The down-street lady was a widow also, the portly, comely relict of our drunken village blacksmith, who, in spite of her joy at her first husband's death, and an old spite at mine host of the Rose, to whose good ale and good company she was wont to ascribe most of the aberrations of the deceased, began to find her shop, her journeymen, and her eight children (six unruly, obstreperous Pickles of boys, and two tom-boys of girls), rather more than a lone woman could manage, and to sigh for a helpmate to ease her of her cares, collect the boys at night, see the girls to school of a morning, break the larger imps of running away to revels and fairs, and the smaller fry of birds-nesting and orchard-robbing, and bear a part in the lectures and chastisements, which she deemed necessary to preserve the young rebels from the bad end which she predicted to them twenty times a day. Master Sims was the coadjutor on whom she had inwardly pitched; and, accordingly, she threw out broad hints to that effect, every time she encountered him, which, in the course of her search for boys and girls, who were sure to be missing at school-time and bedtime, happened pretty often; and Mr Sims was far too gallant and too much in the habit of assenting to listen unmoved; for really the widow was a fine, tall, comely woman; and the whispers, and smiles, and hand-pressings, when they happened to meet, were becoming very tender; and his admonitions and head-shakings addressed to the young crew (who, nevertheless, all liked him) quite fatherly. This was his down-street flame.

The rival lady was Miss Lydia Day, the carpenter's sister; a slim, upright maiden, not remarkable for beauty, and not so young as she had been, who, on inheriting a small annuity from the mistress with whom she had spent the best of her days, retired to her native village to live on her means. A genteel, demure, quiet personage was Miss Lydia Day; much addicted to snuff and green tea, and not averse from a little gentle scandal—for the rest, a good sort of woman, and *un très bon parti* for Master Sims, who seemed to consider it a profitable speculation, and made love to her whenever she happened to come into his head, which, it must be confessed, was hardly so often as her merits and her annuity deserved. Remiss as he was, he had no lack of encouragement to complain of—for she " to hear would seriously incline," and put on her best silk, and her best simper, and lighted up her faded complexion into something approaching to a blush, whenever he came to visit her. And this was Master Sims's up-street love.

So stood affairs at the Rose when the day of the Maying arrived; and the double flirtation, which, however dexterously managed, must have been sometimes, one would think, rather inconvenient to the inamorato, proved on this occasion extremely useful. Each of the fair ladies contributed her aid to the festival; Miss Lydia by tying up sentimental garlands for the May-house, and scolding the carpenters into diligence in the erection of the booths; the widow by giving her whole bevy of boys and girls a holiday, and turning them loose on the neighbourhood to collect flowers as they could. Very useful auxiliaries were these light foragers; they scoured the country far and near—irresistible mendicants! pardonable thieves! coming to no harm, poor children, except that little George got a black eye in tumbling from the top of an acacia-tree at the Park, and that Sam (he's a sad Pickle is Sam!) narrowly escaped a horse-whipping from the head gardener at the Hall, who detected a bunch of his new rhododendron, the only plant in the county, forming the very crown and centre of the May-pole. Little harm did they do, poor children, with all their pilfery; and when they returned, covered with their flowery loads, like the May-day figure called " Jack of the Green," they worked at the garlands and the May-houses, as none but children ever do work, putting all their young life and their untiring spirit of noise and motion into their pleasant labour. Oh, the din of that building! Talk of the Tower of Babel! that was a quiet piece of masonry compared to the May-house of Whitley-wood, with its walls of leaves and flowers—and its canvass booths at either end for refreshments and musicians. Never was known more joyous note of preparation.

The morning rose more quietly—I had almost said more dully—and promised ill for the *fête*. The sky was gloomy, the wind cold, and the green filled as slowly as a balloon seems to do when one is watching it. The entertainments of the day were to begin with a cricket match (two elevens to be chosen on the ground), and the wickets pitched at twelve o'clock precisely. Twelve o'clock came—but no cricketers—except, indeed, some two or three punctual and impatient gentlemen; one o'clock came, and brought no other reinforcement than two or three more of our young Etonians and Wykhamites— less punctual than their precursors, but not a whit less impatient. Very provoking, certainly—but not very uncommon. Your country cricketer, the peasant, the mere rustic, does love, on these occasions, to keep his betters waiting, if only to display his power; and when we consider that it is the one solitary opportunity in which importance can be felt and vanity gratified, we must acknowledge it to be perfectly in human nature that a few airs should be shown. Accordingly, our best players held aloof. Tom Coper would not come to the ground; Joel

Brent came, indeed, but would not play; Samuel Long co-quetted—he would and he would not. Very provoking, certainly! Then two young farmers, a tall brother and a short, Hampshire men, cricketers born, whose good-humour and love of the game rendered them sure cards, had been compelled to go on business—the one, ten miles south—the other, fifteen north—that very morning. No playing without the Goddards! No sign of either of them on the B—— road or the F——. Most intolerably provoking, beyond a doubt! Master Sims tried his best coaxing and his best double X on the recusant players; but all in vain. In short, there was great danger of the match going off altogether; when, about two o'clock, Amos Stone, who was there with the crown of his straw hat sewed in wrong side outward—new thatched, as it were—and who had been set to watch the B—— highway, gave notice that something was coming as tall as the May-pole—which something turning out to be the long Goddard, and his brother approaching at the same moment in the opposite direction, hope, gaiety, and good-humour revived again; and two elevens, including Amos and another urchin of his calibre, were formed on the spot.

I never saw a prettier match. The gentlemen, the Goddards, and the boys being equally divided, the strength and luck of the parties were so well balanced that it produced quite a neck-and-neck race, won only by two notches. Amos was completely the hero of the day, standing out half of his side, and getting five notches at one hit. His side lost—but so many of his opponents gave him their ribands (have not I said that Master Sims bestowed a set of ribands?) that the straw hat was quite covered with purple trophies; and Amos, stalking about the ground, with a shy and awkward vanity, looked with his decorations like the sole conqueror—the Alexander or Napoleon of the day. The boy did not speak a word; but every now and then he displayed a set of huge white teeth in a grin of inexpressible delight. By far the happiest and proudest personage of that Maying was Amos Stone.

By the time the cricket match was over, the world began to be gay at Whitley-wood. Carts and gigs, and horses and carriages, and people of all sorts, arrived from all quarters; and, lastly, " the blessed sun himself " made his appearance, adding a triple lustre to the scene. Fiddlers, ballad-singers, cake baskets—Punch—Master Frost, crying cherries—a French-

man with dancing dogs—a Bavarian woman selling brooms—
half a dozen stalls with fruit and frippery—and twenty noisy
games of quoits, and bowls, and ninepins—boys throwing at
boxes—girls playing at ball—gave to the assemblage the bustle,
clatter, and gaiety of a Dutch fair, as one sees it in Teniers'
pictures. Plenty of drinking and smoking on the green—plenty
of eating in the booths: the gentlemen cricketers, at one end,
dining off a round of beef, which made the table totter—the
players, at the other, supping off a gammon of bacon—Amos

Stone crammed at both—and Landlord Sims bustling everywhere with an activity that seemed to confer upon him the gift
of ubiquity, assisted by the little light-footed maidens, his
daughters, all smiles and curtsies, and by a pretty black-eyed
young woman—name unknown—with whom, even in the midst
of his hurry, he found time, as it seemed to me, for a little
philandering. What would the widow and Miss Lydia have
said? But they remained in happy ignorance—the one drinking tea in most decorous primness in a distant marquee, dis-
liking to mingle with so mixed an assembly—the other in full
chase after the most unlucky of all her urchins, the boy called
Sam, who had gotten into a *démêlé* with a showman, in consequence of mimicking the wooden gentleman Punch, and
his wife Judy—thus, as the showman observed, bringing his
exhibition into disrepute.

Meanwhile, the band struck up in the May-house, and the
dance, after a little demur, was fairly set afloat—an honest
English country dance—(there had been some danger of waltz-
ing and quadrilling)—with ladies and gentlemen at the top,
and country lads and lasses at the bottom; a happy mixture

of cordial kindness on the one hand, and pleased respect on the other. It was droll though to see the beplumed and beflowered French hats, the silks and the furbelows, sailing and rustling amidst the straw bonnets and cotton gowns of the humbler dancers; and not less so to catch a glimpse of the little lame clerk, shabbier than ever, peeping through the canvas opening of the booth, with a grin of ineffable delight, over the shoulder of our vicar's pretty wife. Really, considering that Mabel Green and Jem Tanner were standing together at that moment at the top of the set, so deeply engaged in making love that they forgot when they ought to begin, and that the little clerk must have seen them, I cannot help taking his grin for a favourable omen to those faithful lovers.

Well, the dance finished, the sun went down, and we departed. The Maying is over, the booths carried away, and the May-house demolished. Everything has fallen into its old position, except the love affairs of Landlord Sims. The pretty lass with the black eyes, who first made her appearance at Whitley-wood, is actually staying at the Rose Inn, on a visit to his daughters; and the village talk goes that she is to be the mistress of that thriving hostelry, and the wife of its master; and both her rivals are jealous, after their several fashions—the widow in the tantrums, the maiden in the dumps. Nobody knows exactly who the black-eyed damsel may be—but she's young, and pretty, and civil, and modest; and, without intending to depreciate the merits of either of her competitors, I cannot help thinking that our good neighbour has shown his taste.

THE MOLE-CATCHER

THERE are no more delightful or unfailing associations than those afforded by the various operations of the husbandman, and the changes on the fair face of nature. We all know that busy troops of reapers come with the yellow corn; whilst the yellow leaf brings a no less busy train of ploughmen and seedsmen preparing the ground for fresh harvests; that woodbines and wild roses, flaunting in the blossomy hedgerows, give token of the gay bands of haymakers which enliven the meadows; and that the primroses, which begin to unfold their pale stars by the side of the green lanes, bear marks of the slow and weary female processions, the gangs of tired yet talkative bean-setters, who defile twice a day through the intricate mazes of our cross-country roads. These are general associations, as well known and as universally recognised as the union of mince-pies and Christmas. I have one, more private and peculiar, one, perhaps, the more strongly impressed on my mind, because the impression may be almost confined to myself. The full flush of violets which, about the middle of March, seldom fails to perfume the whole earth, always brings to my recollection one solitary and silent coadjutor of the husbandman's labours, as unlike a violet as possible—Isaac Bint, the mole-catcher.

I used to meet him every spring, when we lived at our old house, whose park-like paddock, with its finely-clumped oaks and elms, and its richly-timbered hedgerows, edging into wild, rude, and solemn fir-plantations, dark, and rough, and hoary, formed for so many years my constant and favourite walk. Here, especially under the great horse-chestnut, and where the bank rose high and naked above the lane, crowned only with a tuft of golden broom; here the sweetest and prettiest of wild flowers, whose very name hath a charm, grew like a carpet under one's feet, enamelling the young green grass with their white and purple blossoms, and loading the air with their delicious fragrance; here I used to come almost every morning, during the violet-tide; and here almost every morning I was sure to meet Isaac Bint.

I think that he fixed himself the more firmly in my memory

by his singular discrepancy with the beauty and cheerfulness of the scenery and the season. Isaac is a tall, lean, gloomy personage with whom the clock of life seems to stand still. He has looked sixty-five for these last twenty years, although his dark hair and beard, and firm manly stride, almost contradict the evidence of his sunken cheeks and deeply-lined forehead. The stride is awful: he hath the stalk of a ghost. His whole air and demeanour savour of one that comes from under ground. His appearance is " of the earth, earthy." His clothes, hands, and face are of the colour of the mould in which he delves. The little round traps which hang behind him over one shoulder, as well as the strings of dead moles which embellish the other, are incrusted with dirt like a tombstone; and the staff which he plunges into the little hillocks, by which he traces the course of his small quarry, returns a hollow sound, as if tapping on the lid of a coffin. Images of the church-yard come, one does not know how, with his presence. Indeed he does officiate as assistant to the sexton in his capacity of grave-digger, chosen, as it should seem, from a natural fitness; a fine sense of congruity in good Joseph Reed, the functionary in question, who felt, without knowing why, that, of all men in the parish, Isaac Bint was best fitted to that solemn office.

His remarkable gift of silence adds much to the impression produced by his remarkable figure. I don't think that I ever heard him speak three words in my life. An approach of that bony hand to that earthy leather cap was the greatest effort of courtesy that my daily salutations could extort from him. For this silence, Isaac has reasons good. He hath a reputation to support. His words are too precious to be wasted. Our mole-catcher, ragged as he looks, is the wise man of the village, the oracle of the village inn, foresees the weather, charms away agues, tells fortunes by the stars, and writes notes upon the almanack—turning and twisting about the predictions after a fashion so ingenious, that it is a moot point which is oftenest wrong—Isaac Bint or Francis Moore. In one eminent instance, our friend was, however, eminently right. He had the good luck to prophesy, before sundry witnesses—some of them sober —in the tap-room of the Bell—he then sitting, pipe in mouth, on the settle at the right-hand side of the fire, whilst Jacob Frost occupied the left—he had the good fortune to foretell, on New Year's Day 1812, the downfall of Napoleon Buonaparte—a piece of soothsayership which has established his reputation, and dumbfounded all doubters and cavillers, ever since; but which would certainly have been more striking if he had not annually uttered the same prediction, from the same place, from the time that the aforesaid Napoleon became first consul. But this small circumstance is entirely overlooked by Isaac and his admirers, and they believe in him, and he believes in the stars, more firmly than ever.

Our mole-catcher is, as might be conjectured, an old bachelor. Your married man hath more of this world about him—is less, so to say, planet-struck. A thorough old bachelor is Isaac, a contemner and maligner of the sex, a complete and decided woman-hater. Female frailty is the only subject on which he hath ever been known to dilate; he will not even charm away their agues, or tell their fortunes, and, indeed, holds them to be unworthy the notice of the stars.

No woman contaminates his household. He lives on the edge of a pretty bit of woodland scenery called the Penge, in a snug cottage of two rooms, of his own building, surrounded by a garden cribbed from the waste, well fenced with quickset, and well stocked with fruit-trees, herbs, and flowers. One large apple-tree extends over the roof—a pretty bit of colour when in blossom, contrasted with the thatch of the little dwelling, and relieved by the dark wood behind. Although the owner be solitary, his demesne is sufficiently populous. A long row of beehives extends along the warmest side of the garden—for Isaac's honey is celebrated far and near; a pig occupies a commodious stye at one corner; and large flocks of ducks and geese (for which the Penge, whose glades are intersected by water, is famous) are generally waiting round a back gate leading to a spacious shed, far larger than Isaac's own cottage, which serves for their feeding and roosting-place. The great tameness of all these creatures—for the ducks and geese flutter round him the moment he approaches, and the very pig follows him like a dog —gives no equivocal testimony of the kindness of our mole-catcher's nature. A circumstance of recent occurrence puts his humanity beyond a doubt.

Amongst the probable causes of Isaac's dislike to women may be reckoned the fact of his living in a female neighbourhood (for the Penge is almost peopled with duck-rearers and goose-crammers of the duck and goose gender), and being himself

N

exceedingly unpopular amongst the fair poultry-feeders of that watery vicinity. He beat them at their own weapons; produced at Midsummer geese fit for Michaelmas; and raised ducks so precocious that the gardeners complained of them as forerunning their vegetable accompaniments; and " panting *peas* toiled after them in vain." In short, the Naïads of the Penge had the mortification to find themselves driven out of B—— market by an interloper, and that interloper a man who had no manner of right to possess any skill in an accomplishment so exclusively feminine as duck-rearing; and being no ways inferior in another female accomplishment, called scolding, to their sister-nymphs of Billingsgate, they set up a clamour and a cackle which might rival the din of their own gooseries at feeding-time, and would inevitably have frightened from the field any competitor less impenetrable than our hero. But Isaac is not a man to shrink from so small an evil as female objurgation. He stalked through it all in mute disdain—looking now at his mole-traps, and now at the stars—pretending not to hear, and very probably not hearing. At first this scorn, more provoking than any retort, only excited his enemies to fresh attacks; but one cannot be always answering another person's silence. The flame which had blazed so fiercely at last burnt itself out, and peace reigned once more in the green alleys of Penge-wood.

One, however, of his adversaries—his nearest neighbour—still remained unsilenced.

Margery Grover was a very old and poor woman, whom age and disease had bent almost to the earth; shaken by palsy, pinched by penury, and soured by misfortune — a moving bundle of misery and rags. Two centuries ago she would have been burnt for a witch; now she starved and grumbled on the parish allowance; trying to eke out a scanty subsistence by the dubious profits gained from the produce of two geese and a lame gander, once the unmolested tenants of a greenish pool, situate right between her dwelling and Isaac's, but whose watery dominion had been invaded by his flourishing colony.

This was the cause of feud; and although Isaac would willingly, from a mingled sense of justice and of pity, have yielded the point to the poor old creature, especially as ponds are there almost as plentiful as blackberries, yet it was not so easy to control the habits and inclinations of their feathered subjects, who all perversely fancied that particular pool; and various accidents and skirmishes occurred, in which the ill-fed and weak birds of Margery had generally the worst of the fray. One of her early goslings was drowned—an accident which may happen even to water-fowl; and her lame gander, a sort of pet with the poor old woman, injured in his well leg; and Margery vented curses as bitter as those of Sycorax; and Isaac, certainly the most superstitious personage in the parish—the most thorough believer in his own gifts and prediction—was fain to nail a horse-shoe on his door for the defence of his property, and to wear one of his own ague charms about his neck for his personal protection.

Poor old Margery! A hard winter came; and the feeble, tottering creature shook in the frosty air like an aspen-leaf; and the hovel in which she dwelt—for nothing could prevail on her to try the shelter of the workhouse—shook like herself at every blast. She was not quite alone either in the world or in her poor hut: husband, children, and grandchildren had passed away; but one young and innocent being, a great-grandson, the last of her descendants, remained, a helpless dependent on one almost as helpless as himself.

Little Harry Grover was a shrunken, stunted boy of five years old; tattered and squalid, like his grandame, and, at first sight, presented almost as miserable a specimen of childhood as Margery herself did of age. There was even a likeness between them; although the fierce blue eye of Margery had, in the boy, a mild appealing look, which entirely changed the whole expression of the countenance. A gentle and a peaceful boy was Harry, and, above all, a useful. It was wonderful how many ears of corn in the autumn, and sticks in the winter, his little hands could pick up! how well he could make a fire, and boil the kettle, and sweep the hearth, and cram the goslings! Never was a handier boy or a trustier; and when the united effects of cold, and age, and rheumatism confined poor Margery to her poor bed, the child continued to perform his accustomed offices; fetching the money from the vestry, buying the loaf at the baker's, keeping house, and nursing the sick woman, with a kindness and thoughtfulness which none but those who know the careful ways to which necessity trains cottage children would deem credible; and Margery, a woman of strong passions, strong prejudices, and strong affections, who had lived in and for the desolate boy, felt the approach of death imbittered by the certainty that the workhouse, always the scene of her dread and loathing, would be the only refuge for the poor orphan.

Death, however, came on visibly and rapidly; and she sent for the overseer to beseech him to put Harry to board in some decent cottage; she could not die in peace until he had promised; the fear of the innocent child's being contaminated by wicked boys and godless women preyed upon her soul; she implored, she conjured. The overseer, a kind but timid man, hesitated, and was beginning a puzzled speech about the bench and the vestry, when another voice was heard from the door of the cottage.

" Margery," said our friend Isaac, " will you trust Harry to me? I am a poor man, to be sure; but, between earning and saving, there'll be enough for me and little Harry. 'Tis as good a boy as ever lived, and I'll try to keep him so. Trust him to me, and I'll be a father to him. I can't say more."

" God bless thee, Isaac Bint! God bless thee! " was all poor Margery could reply.

They were the last words she ever spoke. And little Harry is living with our good mole-catcher, and is growing plump and rosy; and Margery's other pet, the lame gander, lives and thrives with them too.

NEXT in beauty to the view over the Loddon at Aberleigh, is that from Lanton Bridge up and down the clear and winding Kennet, and this present season (the latter end of April) is perhaps the time of year which displays to the greatest advantage that fine piece of pastoral scenery. And yet it is a species of beauty difficult to convey to the reader. There is little to describe but much to feel; the sweet and genial repose of the landscape harmonizes so completely with the noontide sunshine and the soft balmy air. The river, bright and glassy, glides in beautiful curves through a rich valley of meadow land, the view on one side of the bridge terminating at the distance of a couple of miles by the picturesque town of B. with its old towers and spires, whilst on the other the stream seems gradually to lose itself amongst the richly wooded and finely undulating grounds of Lanton Park.

But it is in the meadows themselves that the real charm is to be found: the fresh sprouting grass, bordered with hedgerows just putting on their tenderest green, dotted with wild patches of willow-trees and clumps of noble elms, gay with the golden marsh-marigold and the elegant fritillary; [1] alive with bees and butterflies, and the shining tribe of water insects; and musical with the notes of a countless variety of birds, who cease singing, or whom we cease to listen to (it comes exactly to the same thing), the moment the nightingale begins her matchless song. Here and there, too, farm-houses and cottages, half hidden by cherry orchards just in their fullest bloom, come cranking into the meadows; and farther in the distance chimney-tops with curling wreaths of blue smoke, or groups of poplar, never seen but near dwellings, give a fresh interest to the picture by the unequivocal signs of human habitation and human sympathy.

In one of the nearest of these poplar clumps—not above half a mile off, if it were possible for any creature except a bird to pass the wide deep ditches which intersect these water meadows,

[1] The country people call this beautiful plant the Turkey-egg flower, and indeed the chequered pendant blossoms do, both in their shape and in their mottled tinting, bear some resemblance to the dappled eggs of that stately bird.

but which, by thridding the narrow and intricate lanes that form the only practicable route, we contrive to make nearly six times as long—in that island of spiral poplars and gigantic fruit trees, with one corner of the roof just peeping amongst the blossomy cherry boughs, stands the comfortable abode of my good friend Matthew Shore, to whose ample farm a large portion of these rich meadows forms an appendage of no trifling value.

Matthew is of an old yeomanry family, who have a pedigree of their own, and are as proud of having been for many generations the hereditary tenants of the owners of Lanton Park, as they themselves may be of having been for more centuries than I choose to mention the honoured possessors of that fair estate. Excellent landlords, and excellent tenants, both parties are, I believe, equally pleased with the connexion, and would no more think of dissolving the union, which time and mutual service have cemented so closely, than of breaking through the ties of near relationship; although my friend Matthew, having no taste for agricultural pursuits, his genius for the cultivation of land having broken out in a different line, has devolved on his younger brother Andrew the entire management and superintendence of the farm.

Matthew and Andrew Shore are as unlike as two brothers well can be in all but their strong manly affection for each other, and go on together all the better for their dissimilarity of taste and character. Andrew is a bluff, frank, merry Benedict, blest in a comely bustling wife and five rosy children; somewhat too loud and boisterous in his welcomings, which come upon one like a storm, but delightful in his old-fashioned hospitality and his hearty good-humour; for the rest, a good master, a steady friend, a jovial neighbour, and the best farmer and most sagacious dealer to be found in the countryside. He must be a knowing hand who takes in Andrew Shore. He is a bold rider too, when the foxhounds happen to come irresistibly near; and is famous for his breed of cocking spaniels, and for constantly winning the yeomanry cup at the B. coursing meeting. Such is our good neighbour Farmer Shore.

His wife is not a little like her husband; a laughing, bustling, good-humoured woman, famous for the rearing of turkeys and fattening of calves, ruling the servants and children within doors, with as absolute a discretion as that with which he sways the out-door sceptre, and complaining occasionally of the power she likes so well, and which, with an ingratitude not uncommon in such cases, she is pleased to call trouble. In spite of these complaints, however, she is one of the happiest women in the parish, being amongst the very few who are neither troubled by poverty nor finery—the twin pests of the age and country. Her expenses are those of her grandmother's days; she has fourteen-shilling hyson, and double-refined sugar, for any friend who may drop in to tea, and a handsome silk gown to wear to Church on Sundays. An annual jaunt to Ascot is all her dissipation, and a taxed cart her sole equipage. Well may Mrs Shore be a happy woman.

The only spot about the place sacred from her authority is that which I am come to visit—the garden; my friend Matthew's territory, in which he spends all his days, and half his nights, and which, in spite of his strong fraternal affection, he certainly loves better than brother or sister, nephew or niece, friend or comrade; better, in short, than he loves anything else under the sun.

Matthew is an old bachelor of fifty-five, or there-away, with a quick eye, a ruddy cheek, a delightful benevolence of countenance, a soft voice, and a gentle manner. He is just what he seems, the kindest, the most generous, and the best-natured creature under the sun, the universal friend and refuge of servants, children, paupers, and delinquents of all descriptions, who fly to him for assistance and protection in every emergency, and would certainly stun him with their clamorous importunity if he were not already as deaf as a post.

Matthew is one of the few very deaf people worth talking to. He is what is becoming scarcer every day, a florist of the first order, and of the old school—not exactly of Mr Evelyn's time, for in the gardening of that period, although greens were, flowers were not—but of thirty or forty years back, the reign of pinks, tulips, auriculas, and ranunculuses, when the time and skill of the gardener were devoted to produce, in the highest imaginable perfection, a variety of two or three favoured tribes. The whole of this large garden, for the potatoes and cabbages have been forced to retreat to a nook in the orchard, dug up in their behoof—the whole ample garden is laid out in long beds, like those in a nursery ground, filled with these precious flowers, of the rarest sorts and in the highest culture; and as I have arrived in the midst of the hyacinth, auricula, and anemone season, with the tulips just opening, I may consider myself in great luck to see what is called, in gardening language, " so grand a show." It is worth something, too, to see Matthew's delight, half compounded of vanity and kindness, as he shows them, mixed with courteous offers of seedlings and offsets, and biographical notices of the more curious flowers: " How the stock of this plant came from that noted florist Tom Bonham, the B. tailor, commonly called Tippling Tom, who once refused fifty guineas for three auriculas! and how this tulip was filched " (Matthew tells this in a particularly low and confidential tone) " from a worthy merchant of Rotterdam, by an honest skipper of his acquaintance, who abstracted the root, but left five pounds in the place of it, and afterwards made over the bargain for a couple of pounds more, just to pay him for the grievous bodily fear which he had undergone between the time of this adventure, for there was no telling how the Burgomaster might relish the bargain, and his embarkation in the good schooner the *Race-horse* of Liverpool."

Perhaps the tulips, especially this pet root, are on the whole Matthew's favourites; but he is a great man at pink shows and melon feasts, and his carnations, particularly those of a sort called " the mount Etna," which seldom comes to good in other hands, as regularly win the plate as Andrew's greyhounds. It is quite edifying to hear him run over the bead-roll of pink names, from Cleopatra to the Glory of New York. The last-mentioned flowers are precisely my object to-day; for I am come to beg some of his old plants, to the great endangerment of my character as a woman of taste, I having, sooth to say, no judgment in pinks, except preferring those which are full of bloom, in which quality these old roots, which he was about to fling away, and which he is giving me with a civil reluctance to put anything so worthless into my garden, greatly excel the young plants of which he is so proud.

Notwithstanding his love for his own names, some of which are fantastical enough, Matthew wages fierce war against the cramp appellations, whether of geraniums or of other plants, introduced latterly, and indeed against all new flowers of every sort whatsoever, comprehending them all under the general denomination of trash. He contrives to get the best and the rarest, notwithstanding, and to make them blow better than anybody, and I would lay a wager—Ay, I am right! the rogue! the rogue! What is that in the window but the cactus speciosissimus, most splendid of flowers, with its large ruby cup and its ivory tassels? It is not in bloom yet, but it is showing strong and coming fast. And is not that fellow the scarlet potentilla? And that the last fuchsia? And is there such a plant in the county as that newest of all the new camellias? Ah the rogue! the rogue! He to abuse my geraniums, and call me new-fangled, with four plants in his windows that might challenge the horticultural! And when I laugh at him about it, he'll pretend not to hear, and follow the example of that other great deaf artist,

> Who shifted his trumpet and only took snuff.

Ah the rogue! the rogue! To think that fickleness should be so ingrafted in man's nature, that even Matthew Shore is not able to resist the contagion, but must fall a-flirting with cactuses and camellias—let the pinks and tulips look to it! The rogue! the rogue!

If the fickleness of man were my first thought, the desire to see the camellia nearer was the second; and Mrs Shore appearing in the porch with her clean white apron and her pleasant smile, I followed her through a large, lightsome, bricked apartment, the common room of the family, where the ample hearth, the great chairs in the chimney corner, defended from draughts by green stuff curtains, the massive oak tables, the tall japanned clock, and the huge dresser laden with pewter dishes as bright as silver, gave token of rustic comfort and opulence. Ornaments were not wanting. The dresser was also adorned with the remains of a long-preserved set of tea-china, of a like rambling pattern, consisting of five cups and seven saucers, a tea-pot, neatly mended, a pitcher-like cream-jug, cracked down the middle, and a sugar basin wanting a handle; with sundry odd plates, delf, blue and white, brown-edged and green-edged, scalloped and plain; and last and choicest, with a grand collection of mugs—always the favourite object of housewifely vanity in every rank of rural life, from Mrs Shore of Lanton Farm down to her maid Debby. This collection was of a particularly ambitious nature. It filled a row and a half of the long dresser, graduated according to size, like books in a library, the gallons ranking as folios, the half-pints ranging as duodecimos. Their

number made me involuntarily repeat to myself two lines from
Anstey's inimitable *Pleader's Guide*, meant to ridicule the fictions
of the law, but here turned into a literal truth:

> First count's for that with divers jugs,
> To wit, twelve pots, twelve cups, twelve mugs :

but these jugs were evidently not meant to be profaned by the
" certain vulgar drink called toddy," or any other drink. Half
a dozen plain white ones, rather out of condition, which stood
on a side table, were clearly the drudges, the working mugs of
the family. The ornamental species, the drone mugs, hung on
nails by their handles, and were of every variety of shape,
colour, and pattern. Some of the larger ones were adorned
with portraits in medallion—Mr Wilberforce, Lord Nelson, the
Duke of Wellington, and Charles Fox. Some were gay with
flowers not very like nature. Some had landscapes in red, and
one a group of figures in yellow. Others again, and these were
chiefly the blues, had patterns of all sorts of intricacy and in-
volution without any visible meaning. Some had borders of
many colours; and some, which looked too genteel for their
company, had white cameos relieved on a brown ground.
Those drinking vessels were full of the antique elegance and
grace. I stood admiring them when Mrs Shore called me into
the parlour, where the plant I wished to see was placed.

The parlour—oh how incomparably inferior to the kitchen!
—was a little low, square, dark box into which we were shut
by a door, painted black, dimly lighted by a casement window,
quite filled by the superb camellia, and rendered even more
gloomy by a dark paper of reds and greens, with an orange
border. A piece of furniture called a beaufette, open and displaying a collection of glass-ware almost equal to the pewter
for age and brightness, to the mugs for variety, and to the
china for joinery, a shining round mahogany table, and six
hair-bottomed chairs, really seemed to crowd the little apartment; but it was impossible to look at anything except the
splendid plant, with its dark shining leaves, and the pure, yet
majestic blossoms reposing on the deep verdure, as a pearly
coronet on the glossy locks of some young beauty. Ah! no
wonder that the pinks are a little out of favour, or that Matthew
stands smiling there in utter oblivion of striped tulip or streaked
carnation! such a plant as this would be an excuse for for-

getting the whole vegetable creation, and my good friend Matthew (who always contrives to hear the civil things one says of his flowers, however low one may speak, and who is perfectly satisfied by my admiration on the present occasion) has just made me almost as happy as himself, by promising to rear me one of the same sort, after a method of his own discovering, which he assures me brings them to perfection twice as fast as the dawdling modes of the new school. Nothing like an old gardener after all! above all, if he be as kind, as enthusiastic, and as clever, as my friend Matthew Shore.

IT was a glorious June morning; and I got up gay and bright, as the Americans say, to breakfast in the pretty summer-room overlooking the garden, which, built partly for my accommodation and partly for that of my geraniums, who make it their winter residence, is as regularly called the greenhouse as if I and my several properties—sofas, chairs, tables, chiffoniers, and ottomans—did not inhabit it during the whole of the fine season; as if it were not in its own person a well-proportioned and spacious apartment, no otherways to be distinguished from common drawing-rooms than by being nearly fronted with glass, about which out-of-door myrtles, passion-flowers, clematis, and the Persian honeysuckle, form a most graceful and varied frame-work, not unlike the festoons of flowers and foliage which one sees round some of the scarce and high-priced tradesmen's cards, and ridotto tickets of Hogarth and Bartolozzi. Large glass folding-doors open into the little garden, almost surrounded by old buildings of the most picturesque form—the buildings themselves partly hidden by clustering vines, and my superb bay-tree, its shining leaves glittering in the sun on one side, whilst a tall pear-tree, garlanded to the very top with an English honeysuckle in full flower, breaks the horizontal line of the low cottage-roof on the other; the very pear-tree being, in its own turn, half concealed by a splendid pyramid of geraniums erected under its shade. Such geraniums! It does not become us poor mortals to be vain—but really, my geraniums! There is certainly nothing but the garden into which Aladdin found his way, and where the fruit was composed of gems, that can compare with them. This pyramid is undoubtedly the great object from the greenhouse; but the common flower-beds which surround it, filled with roses of all sorts, and lilies of all colours, and pinks of all patterns, and campanulas of all shapes, to say nothing of the innumerable tribes of annuals, of all the outlandish names that ever were invented, are not to be despised even beside the gorgeous exotics, which, arranged with the nicest attention to colour and form, so as to combine the mingled charms of harmony and contrast, seem to look down proudly on their humble compeers.

No pleasanter place for a summer breakfast—always a pretty thing, with its cherries, and strawberries, and its affluence of nosegays and posies—no pleasanter place for a summer breakfast-table than my greenhouse! And no pleasanter companion, with whom to enjoy it, than the fair friend, as bright as a rosebud, and as gay as a lark—the saucy, merry, charming Kate, who was waiting to partake our country fare. The birds were singing in the branches; bees, and butterflies, and myriads of gay happy insects were flitting about in the flower-beds; the haymakers were crowding to their light and lively labour in a neighbouring meadow; whilst the pleasant smell of the newly-mown grass was blended with that of a bean-field in full blossom still nearer, and with the thousand odours of the garden—so that sight, and sound, and smell were a rare compound of all that is delightful to the sense and the feeling.

Nor were higher pleasures wanting. My pretty friend, with all her vivacity, had a keen relish of what is finest in literature and in poetry. An old folio edition of that volume of Dryden called his *Fables*, which contains the glorious rifacimenti of parts of Chaucer, and the best of his original poems, happened to be on the table; the fine description of Spring in the opening of the *Flower and the Leaf*, led to the picture of Eden in the *Paradise Lost*, and that again to *Comus*, and *Comus* to Fletcher's *Faithful Shepherdess*, and Fletcher's *Faithful Shepherdess* to Shakspeare, and *As You Like It*. The bees and the butterflies, culling for pleasure or for thrift the sweets of my geraniums, were but types of Kate Leslie and myself roving amidst the poets. This does not sound much like a day of distress; but the evil is to come.

A gentle sorrow did arrive, all too soon, in the shape of Kate Leslie's poney-phaeton, which whisked off that charming person as fast as her two long-tailed Arabians could put their feet to the ground. This evil had, however, substantial consolation in the promise of another visit very soon; and I resumed, in peace and quietness, the usual round of idle occupation which forms the morning employment of a country gentlewoman of small fortune; ordered dinner—minced veal, cold ham, a currant-pudding, and a salad—if anybody happens to be curious on the score of my housekeeping; renewed my beau-pots; watered such of my plants as wanted most; mended my gloves; patted

Dash; looked at *The Times*; and was just sitting down to work, or to pretend to work, when I was most pleasantly interrupted by the arrival of some morning visitors—friends from a distance —for whom, after a hearty welcome and some cordial chat, I ordered luncheon, with which order my miseries began.

" The keys, if you please, ma'am, for the wine and the Kennet ale," said Anne, my female factotum, who rules, as regent, not only the cook, and the under-maid, and the boy, but the whole family, myself included, and is an actual housekeeper in every respect except that of keeping the keys. " The keys, ma'am, if you please," said Anne; and then I found that my keys were not in my right-hand pocket, where they ought to have been, nor in my left-hand pocket, where they might have been, nor in either of my apron-pockets, nor in my work-basket, nor in my reticule—in short, that my keys were lost!

Now these keys were only two in number, and small enough in dimensions; but then the one opened that important part of me, my writing-desk; and the other contained within itself the specific power over every lock in the house, being no other than the key of the key-drawer; and no chance of picking them —for alas! alas! the locks were Bramah's! So, after a few exclamations such as, What can have become of my keys? Has any one seen my keys? Somebody must have run away with my keys!—I recollected that, however consolatory to myself such lamentations might be, they would by no means tend to quench the thirst of my guests. I applied myself vigorously to remedy the evil all I could by applications to my nearest neigh-bours (for time was pressing, and our horse and his master out for the day) to supply, as well as might be, my deficiency. Accordingly I sent to the public-house for their best beer, which, not being Kennet ale, would not go down; and to the good-humoured wives of the shoemaker and the baker for their best wine. Fancy to yourselves a decanter of damson wine arriving from one quarter, and a jug of parsnip wine, fresh from the wood, tapped on purpose, from the other! And this for drinkers of Burgundy and Champagne! Luckily the water was good, and my visitors were good-natured, and comforted me in my affliction, and made a jest of the matter. Really they are a nice family, the Sumners, especially the two young men, to whom I have, they say, taught the taste of spring-water.

This trouble passed over lightly enough. But scarcely were

they gone before the tax-gatherer came for money—locked up in my desk! What will the collector say?—And the justice's clerk for warrants, left under my care by the chairman of the bench, and also safely lodged in the same safe repository. What will their worships say to this delinquency? It will be fortunate if they do not issue a warrant against me in my own person! My very purse was left by accident in that unlucky writing-desk; and when our kind neighbours, the Wrights, sent a

melon, and I was forced to borrow a shilling to give the mess-enger, I could bear my loss no longer, and determined to institute a strict search on the instant.

But before the search could begin in came the pretty little roly-poly Sydneys and Murrays, brats from seven downwards, with their whole train of nurses, and nursery-maids, and nursery-governesses, by invitation, to eat strawberries, and the straw-berries were locked up in a cupboard, the key of which was in the unopenable drawer! And good farmer Brookes, he too called, sent by his honour for a bottle of Hollands—the right Schiedam: and the Schiedam was in the cellar; and the key of the cellar was in the Bramah-locked drawer! And the worthy farmer, who behaved charmingly for a man deprived of his gin, was fain to be content with excuses, like a voter after an election; and the poor children were compelled to put up with promises, like a voter before one; to be sure, they had a few pinks and roses to sweeten their disappointment; but the strawberries were as uncome-at-able as the Schiedam.

At last they were gone; and then began the search in good earnest. Every drawer, not locked, every room that could be entered, every box that could be opened, was ransacked over and over again for these intolerable keys.

All my goods and chattels were flung together in heaps, and then picked over (a process which would make even new things seem disjointed and shabby), and the quantities of trumpery thereby disclosed, especially in the shape of thimbles, needle-cases, pincushions, and scissars, from the different work-baskets, work-boxes, and work-bags (your idle person always abounds in working materials), were astounding. I think there were seventeen pincushions of different patterns—beginning with an old boot and ending with a new guitar. But what was there not? It seemed to me that there were pocketable commodities enough to furnish a second-hand bazaar! Everything was there except my keys.

For four hours did I and my luckless maidens perambulate the house, whilst John, the boy, examined the garden; until we were all so tired that we were forced to sit down from mere weariness. Saving always the first night of one of my tragedies, when, though I pique myself on being composed, I can never manage to sit still; except on such an occasion, I do not think I ever walked so much at one time in my life. At last I flung myself on a sofa in the greenhouse, and began to revolve the possibility of their being still in the place where I had first missed them.

A jingle in my apron-pocket afforded some hope, but it turned out to be only the clinking of a pair of garden-scissars against his old companion, a silver pencil-case—and that prospect faded away. A slight opening in Dryden's heavily-bound volume gave another glimmer of sunshine, but it proved to be occasioned by a sprig of myrtle in *Palamon and Arcite*—Kate Leslie's elegant mark.

This circumstance recalled the recollection of my pretty friend. Could she have been the culprit? And I began to ponder over all the instances of unconscious key-stealing that I had heard of amongst my acquaintance. How my old friend, Aunt Martha, had been so well known for that propensity as to be regularly sought after whenever keys were missing; and my

young friend, Edward Harley, from the habit of twisting something round his fingers during his eloquent talk (people used
to provide another eloquent talker, Madame de Staël, with a
willow-twig for the purpose), had once caught up and carried
away a key, also a Bramah, belonging to a lawyer's bureau,
thereby, as the lawyer affirmed, causing the loss of divers law-
suits to himself and his clients. Neither Aunt Martha nor
Edward had been near the place; but Kate Leslie might be
equally subject to absent fits, and might, in a paroxysm, have
abstracted my keys; at all events it was worth trying. So I
wrote her a note to go by post in the evening (for Kate, I grieve
to say, lives above twenty miles off) and determined to await
her reply, and think no more of my calamity.

A wise resolution! but, like many other wise resolves, easier
made than kept. Even if I could have forgotten my loss, my
own household would not have let me.

The cook, with professional callousness, came to demand
sugar for the currant-pudding—and the sugar was in the store-
room—and the store-room was locked; and scarcely had I recovered from this shock before Anne came to inform me that
there was no oil in the cruet, and that the flask was in the cellar,
snugly reposing, I suppose, by the side of the Schiedam, so that
if for weariness I could have eaten, there was no dinner to eat—
for without the salad who would might take the meat! However, I being alone, this signified little; much less than a
circumstance of which I was reminded by my note to Kate
Leslie, namely, that in my desk were two important letters, one
triple, and franked for that very night; as well as a corrected
proof-sheet for which the press was waiting; and that all these
despatches were to be sent off by post that evening.

Roused by this extremity, I carried my troubles and my
writing-desk to my good friend the blacksmith—a civil intelligent man, who sympathized with my distress, sighed, shook his
head, and uttered the word Bramah!—and I thought my perplexity was nearly at its height, when, as I was wending slowly
homeward, my sorrows were brought to a climax by my being
overtaken by one of the friends whom I admire and honour
most in the world—a person whom all the world admires—who
told me, in her prettiest way, that she was glad to see me so near
my own gate, for that she was coming to drink tea with me.

Here was a calamity! The Lady Mary H., a professed tea-

o

drinker—a green-tea-drinker, one (it was a point of sympathy between us) who took nothing but tea and water, and, therefore, required that gentle and lady-like stimulant in full perfection. Lady Mary come to drink tea with me; and I with nothing better to offer her than tea from the shop—the village shop—bohea, or souchong, or whatever they might call the vile mixture. Tea from the shop for Lady Mary! Ill luck could go no further: it was the very extremity of small distress.

Her ladyship is, however, as kind as she is charming, and bore our mutual misfortune with great fortitude; admired my garden, praised my geraniums, and tried to make me forget my calamity. Her kindness was thrown away. I could not even laugh at myself, or find beauty in my flowers, or be pleased with her for flattering them. I tried, however, to do the honours by my plants; and, in placing a large night-scented stock, which was just beginning to emit its odour, upon the table, I struck against the edge, and found something hard under my belt.

" My keys! my keys! " cried I, untying the riband, and half laughing with delight, as I heard a most pleasant jingle on the floor; and the lost keys, sure enough, they were; deposited there, of course, by my own hand; unfelt, unseen, and unsuspected, during our long and weary search. Since the adventure of my dear friend, Mrs S., who hunted a whole morning for her spectacles whilst they were comfortably perched upon her nose, I have met with nothing so silly and so perplexing.

But my troubles were over—my affliction was at an end.

The strawberries were sent to the dear little girls; and the Schiedam to the good farmer; and the warrants to the clerk. The tax-gatherer called for his money; letters and proof went to the post; and never in my life did I enjoy a cup of Twining's green tea so much as the one which Lady Mary and I took together after my day of distress.

OLD MASTER GREEN
A VILLAGE SKETCH

A PARTICULAR sort of mould, which in this county is scarcely to be found except in the tract of land called Chittling Moor, being wanted to form a compost for that very dear part of my small possessions, my beautiful geraniums, we determined to accompany, or rather to follow, in our pretty pony phaeton, the less aristocratic *cortège*, consisting of two boys with wheelbarrows, and old Master Green with a donkey-cart, who had been despatched to collect it some two hours before.

The day was one of the latest in August, and the weather splendidly beautiful, clear, bright, breezy, sunny. It would have been called too warm by one half of the world, and by the other too cold, which I take to be as near an approach to perfection as our climate, or any climate, can well compass. We had been sitting in our large parlour-like greenhouse; a superb fuchsia, bending with the weight of its own blossoms, reaching almost to the top of the house, on one side of the door, and a splendid campanula, with five distinct stems, covered with large yet delicate lilac bells, on the other; the rich balmy scent of the campanula blending with the exquisite odours of tuberoses, jessamine, mignonette, full-blown myrtles, and the honey-sweet clematis, and looking out on gay beds of the latest flowers, China-asters, dahlias, hydrangeas blue and pink, phlox white and purple, the scarlet lobelia, and the scarlet geranium. In short, all within my little garden was autumn, beautiful autumn.

On the other side of our cottage the season seemed to have changed. The China-roses and honeysuckles, with which it is nearly covered, were in the profuse bloom of early June, and the old monthly rose by the door-way (the sweetest of roses!), together with a cluster of sweet-peas that grew among its branches, were literally smelling of summer. The quantity of rain that had fallen had preserved the trees in their most vivid freshness, and the herbage by the roadside and the shorter turf on the common had all the tender verdure of spring.

As we advanced, however, through the narrow lanes, autumn and harvest reasserted their rights. Every here and there, at the corners where branches jutted out, and in the straits where the hedges closed in together, loose straws of oats and barley, torn from their different waggons, hung dangling from the boughs, mixed with straggling locks of hay, the relics of the after-crop. We ourselves were fain to drive into a ditch, to take shelter from a dingy procession of bean-carriers. My companion, provoked at the ditchy indignity, which his horse relished no better than himself, asserted that the beans could not be fit to carry; but, to judge from the rattling and crackling which the huge black sheaves made in their transit, especially when the loaded wain was jerked a little on one side, to avoid entirely driving over our light and graceful open carriage, which it overtopped, and threatened to crush, as the giant in the fairy tale threatens Tom Thumb—to judge by that noisy indication of ripeness, ripe they were. The hedgerows, too, gave abundant proofs in their own vegetation of the advancing season. The fragrant hazel-nuts were hardening in their shells, and tempting the school-boy's hand by their swelling clusters; the dewberries were colouring; the yellow St John's wort, and the tall mealy-leaved mullein, had succeeded the blushing bells of the foxglove, which, despoiled of its crimson beauty, now brandished its long spikes of seed-vessels upon the bank, above which the mountain-ash waved its scarlet berries in all the glory of autumn; whilst, as we emerged from the close narrow lanes into the open tract of Hartley Common, patches of purple heath just bursting into flower, and the gorse and broom pushing forth fresh blossom under the influence of the late rainy weather, waved over the light harebell, the fragrant thyme, and the springing fungi of the season. In short, the whole of our Berkshire world, as well as that very dear and very tiny bit of it called my garden, spoke of autumn, beautiful autumn, the best if not the only time for a visit to the Chittling Moor.

These Moors were pretty much what the word commonly indicates, a long level tract of somewhat swampy pasture land, extending along the margin of the Kennet, which, in other parts so beautiful, rolled heavily and lazily through its abundant, but somewhat coarse, herbage; a dreary and desolate place when compared with the general scenery of our richly wooded and thickly peopled country, and one where the eye, wandering over the dull expanse, unbroken by hill, or hedge, or timber tree, conveyed, as is often the case in flat, barren, and desolate scenes, an idea of space more than commensurate with the actual extent.

The divisions of this large piece of ground are formed of wide ditches, which at once serve to drain and to irrigate these marshy moors, so frequently overflowed by the river in spring and winter, and sometimes even in summer; it being no unusual catastrophe for the coarse and heavy crops to be carried away by a sudden flood, disappointing the hopes of the farmer, and baffling the efforts of the haymaker. A weary thing was a wet summer in the Chittling Moor, with the hay-field one day a swamp and the next a lake; and the hay, or rather the poor drowned grass, that should have been hay, choking the ditches, or sailing down the stream! The best that could befall it was to be carried off in waggons in its grassy shape, and made comfortably and snugly on dry ground, in some upland meadow; but people cannot always find room for the outer integuments of three hundred acres of grass land, and, besides that difficulty, the intersecting ditches, with their clattering, hollow-sounding wooden bridges, presented no ordinary peril to the heavy wains, so that the landlord was fain to put up with little rent, and the farmer with small profit—too happy if the subsequent grazing paid the charge or the loss of the prolonged and often fruitless hay-harvest.

A dreary scene was the Chittling Moor; a few old willow pollards, the most melancholy of trees, formed the sole break to its dull uniformity, and one small dwelling, whose curling smoke rose in the distance above a clustering orchard, was the only sign of human habitation. This small cottage had been built chiefly to suit the circumstances of the Moor, which rendered a public-house necessary during the long hay-making; and it was kept by a widow, who contrived to make the profits of that watery but drouthy season pay for the want of custom during the rest of the year. Not that the Widow Knight was absolutely without customers at any period; the excellence and celebrity of her home-brewed having insured to her a certain number of customers, who, especially on Sundays, used to walk down to the Chittling Gate (so was her domicile entitled) to partake of the luxuries of a pipe and a pot of ale, scream to the deaf widow, gossip with her comely daughter, or flirt with her pretty grandchild (for the whole establishment was female), as their several ages or dispositions might prompt.

Of this number none was more constant than our present attendant, old Master Green, and it is by no means certain whether his familiarity with the banks and pollards which afforded the true geranium mould may not have been acquired by his hebdomadal visits to the Widow Knight's snug and solitary ale-house.

Old George Green was indeed a veteran of the tap-room, one to whom strong beer had been for nearly seventy years the best friend and the worst enemy, making him happy and keeping him poor. He called himself eighty-five; and I presume, from the report of other people, as well as his own (for when approaching that age, vanity generally takes the turn of making itself older), that he might really be past fourscore. A wonderful man he was of his years, both in appearance and constitution. Hard work had counteracted the ill effects of hard drinking, as an equal quantity of labour, under the form of hard riding, sometimes used to do by a jovial fox-hunting squire of former times, and had kept him light, vigorous, and active, as little bent or stiffened by age as the two boys who were delving out the earth under his direction. The only visible mark which age had set upon him—mark did I say? a brand, a fire-brand—was in his nose, which was of the true Bardolphian size and colour, and a certain roll of the eye, which might perhaps, under any circumstances, have belonged to the man and his humour, but which much resembled that of a toper when half tipsy, and fancying himself particularly wise.

The very Nestor of village topers was Master Green, hearty, good-humoured, merry, and jolly, very civil, and a little sly. He was quite patriarchal in the number of his descendants, having had the Mohammedan allowance of four wives, although, after the Christian fashion, successively, and more children and grandchildren than he could conveniently count. Indeed, his computation varied a little, according as he happened to be drunk or sober; for he was proud of his long train of descendants, just as his betters may be proud of a long line of ancestry; and, being no disciple of the Malthusian doctrine, thought he " had done the state " (that is, the parish) " some service," in rearing up a goodly tribe of sons and daughters, many of them in their turn grandfathers and grandmothers, and most of whom had conducted themselves passably in the world, as times go—thanks probably to a circumstance which he sometimes lamented, their being, men and women, but puny tipplers compared with their jolly progenitor. Even his favourite grandson and namesake, only son and heir of the most prosperous of his innumerous family, Master Green, the thriving carpenter of East Hartley, who, like a dutiful lad, came every Sunday afternoon to the Chittling Gate to meet his grandfather, abandoning for that purpose the cricket-ground at Hartley, where he, a singularly fine young man, had long been accounted the best player—even this favourite grandson was, he declared, little better than a milksop, a swallower of tea and soda-water. " I verily believe," said Master Green, " that a pot of double X would upset him ! "

A friend and a promoter of matrimony in all its shapes, especially in the guise of a love-match, was our worthy greatgrandfather, whether in his own person, or in the person of his descendants. Four wives had he had of happy memory, and he spoke of them all with mingled affection and philosophy, as good sort of women in the main, though the first was somewhat of a slut, the second ugly, the third silly, and the last a scold, which, as he observed, " might be one reason that he missed her so much, poor woman ! the house seemed so quiet and *unked* "—whereupon he sighed, and then, with a roll of his eye and a knowing twist of his Bardolphian nose, began to talk of the necessity of his looking out for a fifth helpmate.

By this time the operation of collecting the geranium mould was in full activity ; and the conversation of the old man and the two lively boys, to which we were authorized listeners, and in which my companion soon became an interlocutor, gave us to understand that they were in possession of some further information respecting Master Green's matrimonial intentions.

" We all know why he goes to the Chittling Gate every Sunday," said Ben, an arch saucy lad, of whom we have before heard in this volume.

"Any child may know that." responded Master Green, trying to look demure and innocent, like a young lady when rallied on her admirers ; " any child can tell that. The Widow Knight brews the best ale in the parish."

" Ay, but that's not the only reason," said John, a modest youth of sixteen : " is it, Ben ? "

" It's reason enough," rejoined Master Green.

" But not *the* reason," retorted Ben.

"What! the widow herself?" quoth my companion.

"Lord, no, sir," interrupted Ben.

"'Twould be a very suitable match, and a snug resting-place, only I'm afraid he would drink up all the ale in the cellar," pursued the interrogator.

"Lord, no, sir!" again exclaimed Ben. "Master Green thinks the widow too old."

"Too old! Why she's a score of years younger than himself, but I suppose he prefers the daughter?"

"No, no, sir," rejoined Ben; "she's too old, too. The granddaughter, the granddaughter! That's the match for Master Green."

"What! the young pretty girl, Susan Parker, a girl of eighteen, marry a man of eighty! nonsense, Ben."

"They've been asked in church, sir," said John quietly; "I heard it myself."

"Asked in church! But I thought the young carpenter was after Susan? Asked in church! Master Green, are you rivalling your own grandson?"

"His father, the sick carpenter, would not hear of that match," cried Ben, "because Susan had no money."

"And what does he say to this match, Ben?"

"Sir, he says that he likes it worse than t'other, but that he can't help this; that his father is an old fool, and must answer for his own folly."

"Well, but Susan! she never can be such a goose. It must be a mistake. Have you really been asked in church, Master Green? Have the banns actually been published?"

"Twice, sir, in full form," answered the old man gravely, "I wonder your honour did not hear them."

"And is the match really to take place?"

"Next Monday, your honour, God willing."

"Pshaw! nonsense! the thing's impossible! you are all joking."

"Time will prove, sir," rejoined Master Green, still more gravely; and, the geranium mould being now fairly collected, we parted.

And on the next Monday the marriage did take place sure enough, though not exactly in the way anticipated, George Green the younger proving to be the bridegroom, to the surprise of bridemaid, parson, and clerk: whilst the rich carpenter, unable to resist the double pleadings of his father and his son, and somewhat pleased to be spared the scandal of so youthful a stepmother, forgave the trick and the stolen match; and old George Green, in the fulness of his delight, got tipsier than ever, in honour of his success, and toasted the Widow Knight so often and so heartily in her own home-brewed, that it's odds but he becomes the landlord of that snug ale-house, the Chittling Gate, after all.

THE HAYMAKERS
A COUNTRY STORY

AMONGST the country employments of England, none is so delightful to see or to think of as hay-making. It comes in the pleasantest season, amidst a green, and flowery, and sunshiny world; it has for scene the prettiest places—park, or lawn, or meadow, or upland pasture; and withal it has more of innocent merriment, more of the festivity of an out-of-door sport, and less of the drudgery and weariness of actual labour, than any other of the occupations of husbandry. One looks on it, pretty picture as it is, without the almost saddening sympathy produced by the slow and painful toil of the harvest field, and, moreover, one looks on it much oftener. A very little interval of dressed garden shall divide a great country mansion from the demesne, where hay-cocks repose under noble groups of oaks and elms, or mingle their fragrance with the snowy wreaths of the acacia, or the honeyed tassels of the lime; and the fair and delicate lady who cannot tell wheat from barley, and the mincing fine gentleman who " affects an *ignorance* if he have it not," shall yet condescend not merely to know hay when they see it, but even to take some interest in the process of getting it up. In short, at the most aristocratic country tables, from the high sheriff of the county to the lord lieutenant, hay is a permitted subject; and the state of the clouds, or of the weatherglass, shall be inquired into as diligently, and be listened to with as much attention, as speculations on the St Leger or the Derby, discussions on the breed of pheasants, or calculations on a contested election. Hay is very naturally felt to be a gentlemanly topic, since from the richest to the poorest every country gentleman is a hay-owner.

I have been used all my life to take a lively interest, and even so much participation as may belong to a mere spectator, in this pleasant labour; for I cannot say that I ever actually handled the fork or the rake. In former times our operations were on a grand scale, since the lawn before and around our old house, and the park-like paddock behind, were of such an extent as to make the getting-in of the crop an affair of considerable moment in a pecuniary point of view. Now we have in our own hands only two small fields, the one a meadow of some three acres, about a mile off, the other a bit of upland pasture not much bigger, and rather nearer. The consequence of which diminution of property is, that I am ten times more interested in our small possession than ever I was in our large demesne, and that the produce of these two little bits of land—the minikin rick, not much better than a hay-cock itself, all of which is to be consumed by that special friend of mine, our pretty frisky cream-coloured horse,[1] of whom it is every day predicted that he will break our necks—appears much more important in my eyes than the mountains of dried grass, which, after feeding some dozen horses, and half a dozen cows, were sold out amongst inn-keepers, coach-proprietors, cattle-dealers, and hay-buyers of all sorts, and sometimes in a plentiful year had even the honour to be advertised in a country newspaper, put up to public sale, puffed by the auctioneer, abused by the bidders, talked about, and lied about, and finally knocked down by the hammer—as great a piece of promotion as a hay-rick can well come to.

This trick of estimating one's possessions in an inverse ratio to their real value is, I believe, strange as the assertion may seem, no uncommon freak of that whimsical, but good for *something* piece of perversity called human nature. In my own case, I can, besides, claim in mitigation for the mistake (if mistake it be to take an interest in anything innocent!), the extreme beauty of the two patches of ground on which grows the hay in question.

One of these grassplots is a breezy, airy, upland field, abutting on the southernmost nook of an open common, forming, so to say, one side of a sunny bay, half filled with a large clear pond of bright water, water always bright; the first swallows of the year are regularly seen there; a great farm-house with its bustling establishment directly opposite; a winding road leading across the green; and trees, cottages, children, horses, cows, sheep, and geese, scattered around in the gayest profusion —a living and moving picture. The most populous street of a populous city gives a less vivid idea of habitation, than the view from the gate, or from the high bank, feathered with broom and hazel—for the fence consists rather of a ditch than of a hedge,

---

[1] Now, alas, no more! Would that the beauty were alive again, even if he did put our lives in jeopardy! I shall never entertain so strong a personal friendship for any steed.

the field being as it were moated—of that lightsome and cheerful bit of pasture land.

The more distant meadow is prettier still; it has no regular approach, and is reached only through a chain of fields belonging to different neighbours, whose gates, close locked upon all other occasions, open only to admit the ponderous hay waggon, creaking under its burthen, and the noisy procession of pitchers and rakers by which it is accompanied. Surrounded by close and high hedges, richly studded by hedgerow timber, no spot can be more completely shut out from the world than this small meadow. A stream of considerable variety and beauty winds along one end, fringed on each margin by little thickets of copse wood, hawthorn, and hazel, mixed with trees of a larger growth, and clothed, intertwisted, matted, by garlands of wild rose and wild honeysuckle; whilst here and there a narrow strip of turf intervenes between these natural shrubberies and the sparkling, glittering, babbling stream, which runs so clearly over its narrow bed that every shoal of minnows is visible as they pass. Every vagary that a nameless brooklet well can play does this brook show off in its short course across the end of our meadow; now driven rapidly through a narrow channel by the curvature of the banks, fretting, and fuming, and chafing over the transparent pebbles; now creeping gently between clusters of the rich willow-herb, and golden flag; now sleeping quietly in a wider and deeper pool, where the white water-lily has found room for its dark leaves and its snowy flowers, and where those quiet but treacherous waters seem about to undermine the grassy margent, which already overhangs them, and to lay bare the roots of the old willows. A tricksy streamlet is that nameless brook, and on the banks of that tricksy stream lies the scene of our little story.

Last summer was, as most of my readers probably remember, one of no small trial to haymakers in general, the weather being what is gently and politely termed " unsettled," which in this pretty climate of ours, during " the leafy month of June," may commonly be construed into cloudy, stormy, drizzly, cold. In this instance the silky, courtly, flattering epithet, being translated, could hardly mean other than wet—fixed, determined, settled rain. From morning to night the clouds were dropping; roses stood tottering on their stalks; strawberries lay sopping in their beds; cherries and currants hung all forlorn on their boughs, with the red juice washed out of them; gravel roads turned into sand; pools into ponds; ditches into rivulets; rivers overflowed their channels; and that great evil a summer flood appeared inevitable. " The rain it raineth every day " was the motto for the month. Sheridan's wicked interpolation in Mr Coleridge's tragedy, " drip, drip, drip, there's nothing here but dripping," seemed made expressly for the season. Cut or uncut, the grass was spoiling; the more the hay was made, the clearer it appeared that it would never make to any purpose; the poor cattle shook their ears as if aware of an impending scarcity; salt, the grand remedy for sopped hay, rose in the market; farmers fretted; and gentlemen fumed.[1]

So passed the " merry month of June." Towards the beginning of July, however, matters mended. A new moon made her appearance in the world, and that great stranger the sun, as if out of compliment to his fair cold sister, ventured out of the clouds to salute her across the sky, one evening just before his usual time of setting, and even continued the civility by leaving behind him such a glow of purple rosiness, and such a line of golden light, as illumined the whole horizon, and gave the most gracious promise for the ensuing day—a promise unusually well kept for so great a personage, that is to say, not quite forgotten. The weather, to be sure, was not quite perfect—when was the weather ever known to be so? it was, on the contrary, of that description which is termed " catching "; but still there were intervals of brightness; the rain was less heavy; the sun did shine sometimes; and even when he refused to show that resplendent face of his, a light stirring breeze answered all haymaking purposes almost as well. In short, between wind and sunshine, we managed to get in our upland crop, with little danger and less damage, and encouraged by that success, and by the slow gentle rising of the weather-glass, which the knowing in such matters affirm to be much more reliable than a sudden and violent jump of the quicksilver, we gave orders to cut the little mead without delay, and prepared for a day's hay-making in that favourite spot.

[1] It is well if they did no worse. A fair young friend of mine, whose father, one of the most accomplished persons that I have ever known, and by no means addicted to the use of naughty words on common occasions, rented about thirty acres of water-meadow, known by the name of " the moors," used always to call the hay-making time his " swearing month." He was wont to laugh at the expression—but I never heard him deny that it was true.

We were not without other encouragements with respect to the weather. The sun himself had had the goodness to make " a golden set," and a rosy dawning, and those vegetable barometers the scarlet pimpernel in the hedgerows, and the purple Venus's looking-glass in the garden, threw open their rich cups to receive his earliest beams, with a fulness of expansion seldom shown by those, I had almost said, sentient flowers, when there is the slightest appearance of rain. Our good neighbour the shoemaker, too, an indoor oracle, whose speculations on the atmosphere are not very remarkable for their correctness, prognosticated wet; whilst our other good neighbour, farmer Bridgwater, an out-of-door practical personage, whose predictions—and it is saying much for them—are almost as sure to come true as the worthy cordwainer's to prove false, boldly asseverated that the day would prove fine, and made his preparations and mustered his troops (for farmer Bridgwater is generalissimo in our hay-field) with a vigour and energy that would have become a higher occasion. He set six men on to mowing by a little after sunrise, and collected fourteen efficient haymakers by breakfast-time. Fourteen active haymakers for our poor three acres! not to count the idle assistants; we ourselves, with three dogs and two boys to mind them, advisers who came to find fault and look on, babies who came to be nursed, children who came to rock the babies, and other children who came to keep the rockers company and play with the dogs; to say nothing of this small rabble, we had fourteen able-bodied men and women in one hay-field, besides the six mowers, who had got the grass down by noon, and, finding the strong beer good and plentiful, magnanimously volunteered to stay and help to get in the crop. N.B. This abundance of aid is by no means so extravagant as it seems, especially in catching weather. Beer, particularly in country affairs, will go twice as far as money, and, if discreetly administered (for we must not make even haymakers quite tipsy), really goes as near to supply the place of the sun as anything well can do. In our case the good double X was seconded by this bright luminary, and our operations prospered accordingly.

Besides being a numerous, ours was a merry group, very merry and very noisy; for amongst the country people, as amongst children, those two words may almost be reckoned synonymous. There was singing that might pass for screaming; laughter that burst forth in peals and in shouts; and talking in every variety of key, from the rough bluff commanding halloo of farmer Bridgwater, issuing his orders from one end of the field to another, to the shrill cry of dame Wilson's baby, which seemed to pierce upwards and cleave the very sky. A mingled buzz of talking was, however, the predominant sound, talking of which little could be collected except a general expression of happiness, dame Wilson's roaring infant being with one exception the only dissatisfied person in the field.

Nobody could imagine the joyous din of that little place. A "jovial crew" they were, though by no means "merry beggars"; for our haymakers were for that profession persons of respectability, rather indeed amateurs than professors— saving perhaps dame Wilson and her set of boys and girls, who might be accounted poor, and a certain ragged Irishman called Jerry, who comes over every year harvesting, and is a general favourite with high and low; with these small drawbacks (N.B. dame Wilson is a mountain of a woman, at least five feet in the girth, and Jerry a maypole of a man, who stands six feet three without his shoes), with these trifling exceptions, our troop of haymakers might really pass for people of substance.

First came the commander-in-chief, farmer Bridgwater, a hearty sturdy old bachelor, rough and bluff and merry and kind, a great although a general admirer of our pretty lasses, to whom his blunt compliments and rustic raillery, of which the point lay rather in a knowing wink, a sly turn of the head, and a peculiar dryness of manner, than in the words, added to his unfailing good nature, rendered him always welcome.

Next in the list figures our respectable neighbour, Aaron Keep the shoemaker, who came to help us and to watch the weather. He is an excellent person is Aaron Keep, and he came, as he said, to help us; and I dare say he would have been very sorry if the hay had been quite spoiled; nevertheless, having pre- dicted that it would rain, I cannot help thinking he considered it a little hard that no rain came. The least little shower, just to confirm his prognostics, would have made him happy, and he kept watching the clouds, and hoping and foretelling a thunderstorm; but the clouds were obstinate, and the more he predicted that a storm would come, the more it stayed away.

Then arrived Master Wheatley, our worthy neighbour the wheelwright, who, being also parish constable, might have abated the noise if he himself had not been the noisiest. I think he came to please his daughter Mary, a smiling airy damsel of thirteen, who never made hay before in her life. How enraptured the little girl was with the holiday! My dog Dash was the only creature in the field gay enough to keep pace with her frolics. They were playmates during the whole day.

Mine host of the Rose was also present, that model of all village landlords, mine host in his red waistcoat; and he also brought with him his pretty daughters, lasses of eighteen and twenty, who care no more for poor Dash than I do for a wax doll; I dare say they don't even know that he's a spaniel. Lucy had been to London this spring, and brought home a beau whom she had picked up there as a visitor to her papa, and, our hay-field being a good place for love-making, there too was he, displaying in handling a prong all the awkwardness that might be expected from a Cheapside haberdasher accustomed to the yard. He laughed at himself, however, with a very good grace, and seemed a well-conditioned and well-behaved person, his misfortune of cockneyism notwithstanding. They said that Miss Lucy would soon leave the Rose and take to measuring ribands herself. Patty too, the round-faced, rosy-cheeked, fair-haired, younger sister, my favourite (but that is a secret, for both are equally civil, and, as far as I know, equally good; I would not make any difference in the world, only—Patty is my favourite); Patty, said the world—the village world, was also not unlikely to leave the Rose, though for an abode only two doors removed from it; Mr George Waring, our smart young saddler, having, they affirmed, won her heart; but upon looking out for Patty and George, thinking to find them engaged as the other couple were, what was my astonishment to see the poor little lass, her smiles gone and her roses faded, moping under the hedge alone, rather making believe to rake than actually raking; whilst Mr George Waring was tossing about the hay in company with the handsome brunette Sally Wheeler, who was just (as I remembered to have heard) come home from service to be married, and looking prodigiously as if the young saddler was her intended spouse. Nothing was ever more suspicious. He looked brighter and gayer than ever, and so did Sally, and for certain they were talking of something interesting, something at which the gentleman smiled and the lady blushed, talking so earnestly that they even forgot to toss the hay about, and that farmer Bridgwater's loudest reprimand, although it startled every one else in the field, was apparently unheard by either of them.

" Alas ! I fear Mr George Waring will play poor Patty false," was my involuntary thought, as I glided amongst the thickets by the side of the stream, and established myself in a verdant nook quite out of sight of the gay scene I had quitted, from which I was parted by a natural shrubbery of honeysuckle and wild roses, covered with blossoms and over-canopied by the spreading branches of a large oak. A pleasant seat was that green bank, with the clear water flowing at my feet, gay with the yellow flag, the white lily, and the blue forget-me-not, and fragrant with the rich tufts of the elegant meadow-sweet, mingling its delicious odour with that of the wild rose, the honeysuckle, and the new-mown hay. A pleasant seat was that turfy bank, and, as the haymakers adjourned to the farther end of the field to dinner, a quiet one; until suddenly I heard first a deep sigh, and then two voices, from the other side of the oak-tree. I listened with somewhat of curiosity, but more of interest, to the following dialogue :—

" Why, my queen," said the bluff good-humoured voice of farmer Bridgwater, " what are you moping here for ? And what have you done with your rosy cheeks ? A'n't you well ? "

" Yes," answered the sighing Patty.

" Go to dinner, then," responded the generalissimo of the hay-field.

" No," sighed the damsel; " I'd rather stay here."

" Shall Lucy bring you something to eat ? " pursued the good farmer.

" No."

" Or your father ? "

" No."

" Or Aaron Keep ? I see he has done."

" No."

" Or little Mary Wheatley ? she'll be here like a bird."

" No, I don't want any dinner, thank you "; and then came a deep sigh—such a sigh !

" Or I myself? " continued the honest farmer, not at all diverted from his purpose.

" No. It's very good of you," said Patty, half crying, " and I am very much obliged—but—"

" Perhaps you'd rather George Waring should bring it? " pursued the pertinacious inquirer, with a slight change of voice. " I'll go and send him directly."

" Don't think of such a thing," interrupted Patty, breathlessly; " he's engaged."

" No," chuckled the farmer, " that business is over; Sally and he have settled the wedding-day, and I have recommended you for bridemaid."

" Me! "

" Ay, you! One wedding leads to another. Wednesday week is to be the day; and after George Waring has given Sally to his brother Tom, he'll have an excellent opportunity for courting you."

" Tom! Tom Waring! Of whom are you speaking? "

" Of George's brother, to be sure, and Sally's beau. There he is, just come into the field. Did you never hear of Tom Waring? He only arrived from Andover last night, where Sally and he have been living next door to each other; and now they are going to marry and settle, as true lovers should. Why, what's the girl crying for? " exclaimed the good farmer, " crying and smiling, and blushing, and looking so happy! Did you think George was making love to her in his own proper person, you goosecap? Will you come to dinner now, you simpleton? you'd better, or I'll tell."

" Oh, farmer Bridgwater! "

" Wipe your eyes and come to dinner, or I'll send George Waring to fetch you; come along, I say."

" Oh, farmer Bridgwater! "—and off they marched; and the next I saw of the haymakers, George and Patty were at work together, and so were Tom and Sally, looking as happy all the four as ever people could do in this world.

FAREWELL TO OUR VILLAGE

WAS it the gentle Addison, as quoted by Johnson, or Johnson himself, that tender heart enclosed in a rough rind, who said that he could not part without sorrow from the stump of an old tree that he had known since he was a boy? Whoever said it, gave utterance to one of the deepest and most universal feelings of our common nature. The attractions of novelty are weak and powerless, in comparison with the minute but strong chains of habit, and the moment of separation is that of all others in which, with an amiable illusion, we brighten and magnify the good qualities of the object we leave, whilst we forget or overlook whatever at another time may have displeased us. The last tone is a tone of kindness; the last look a look of regret.

The very words consecrated to parting embody this sentiment: farewell! adieu! good-bye! Why, they are benedictions, tender, solemn benedictions! How poor and trivial, when measured with their intensity, seem the ordinary phrases of meeting: good day! good morrow! how d'ye do? how are you?[1] These are felt at once to be mere formal ceremonials, sentences of custom, spoken bows and curtseys, as cold and as unmeaning as the compliments at the beginning of a note, or the humble servant at the end of a letter. Even between the most assured friends, there is the same remarkable distinction in manner and in word. We shake hands at meeting, at parting we embrace.

The poets, faithful chroniclers of human feeling, have not failed to resort frequently to a source of sympathy so general and so true: witness the parting of Hector and Andromache in the " tale of Troy divine "; and many of the finest passages in the finest writers, from Homer to Walter Scott. Nay, the feeling itself has made poets, as in the case of Mary Queen of Scots, whose beautiful verses, " adieu, plaisant pays de France! " may be reckoned amongst the tenderest adieux in any language. Perhaps, at no instant of her most unhappy life did that unfortunate Beauty experience a keener sensation of grief than

[1] Mr Spenser's little poem, *One day Good-bye met How-d'ye-do?*, is a pretty illustration of this difference.

when sighing forth that farewell! I doubt, indeed, if farewell can be spoken without some sensation of sorrow.

Nevertheless, it is a word that must in the course of events find utterance from us all; and just now it falls to my lot to bid a late and lingering good-bye to the snug nook called Our Village. The word must be spoken. For ten long years, for five tedious volumes, has that most multifarious and most kind personage, the public, endured to hear the history, half real, and half imaginary, of a half imaginary and half real little spot on the sunny side of Berkshire; but all mortal things have an end, and so must my country stories. The longest tragedy has only five acts; and since the days of Clarissa Harlowe, no author has dreamt of spinning out one single subject through ten weary years. I blush to think how much I have encroached on an indulgence so patient and so kind. Sorry as I am to part from a locality which has become almost identified with myself, this volume must and shall be the last.

Farewell, then, my beloved village! the long straggling street, gay and bright in this sunny, windy April morning, full of all implements of dirt and noise—men, women, children, cows, horses, waggons, carts, pigs, dogs, geese, and chickens, busy, merry, stirring little world, farewell! Farewell to the winding uphill road, with its clouds of dust as horsemen and carriages ascend the gentle eminence, its borders of turf, and its primrosy hedgerows!—Farewell to the breezy common, with its islands of cottages and cottage gardens; its oaken avenues populous with rooks; its clear waters fringed with gorse, where lambs are straying; its cricket-ground where children already linger, anticipating their summer revelry; its pretty boundary of field and woodland, and distant farms; and latest and best of its ornaments, the dear and pleasant mansion where dwell the neighbours of neighbours, the friends of friends; farewell to ye all! Ye will easily dispense with me, but what I shall do without you, I cannot imagine. Mine own dear village, farewell!